The Art Extension Press, Inc.

Boy and Angel

Painted by the American artist ABBOTT H. THAYER.
It is now in possession of the estate of the artist

The World of Music

SONGS OF MANY LANDS

By

MABELLE GLENN
DIRECTOR OF MUSIC, PUBLIC SCHOOLS, KANSAS CITY, MISSOURI

HELEN S. LEAVITT
INSTRUCTOR IN MUSIC, BOSTON UNIVERSITY AND THE WHEELOCK SCHOOL
BOSTON, MASSACHUSETTS

VICTOR L. F. REBMANN
FORMERLY DIRECTOR OF MUSIC, WESTCHESTER COUNTY, NEW YORK

EARL L. BAKER
FORMERLY DIRECTOR OF PUBLIC SCHOOL MUSIC DEPARTMENT
LAWRENCE COLLEGE, APPLETON, WISCONSIN

ART EDITOR
C. VALENTINE KIRBY
STATE DIRECTOR OF ART EDUCATION, PENNSYLVANIA

GINN AND COMPANY

BOSTON · NEW YORK · CHICAGO · LONDON · ATLANTA · DALLAS · COLUMBUS · SAN FRANCISCO

The World of Music

KINDERGARTEN

SING A SONG
PLAY A TUNE

ELEMENTARY GRADES

LISTEN AND SING
TUNING UP
RHYTHMS AND RIMES
SONGS OF MANY LANDS
BLENDING VOICES
TUNES AND HARMONIES

ALL GRADES

SINGING DAYS

836.7

Classified Contents

Special Days

Occupations

Social Relationship

Earth, Sea, and Sky

In the Country

Humor and Nonsense

Games and Sports

Water, Wind, and Weather

Music and the Dance

Citizenship — Character Development

Birds and Animals

Health Songs

Story and Legend

Praise and Thanks

There are here 128 folk songs and 58 composed songs.

Rote Experience: 37 songs, indicated by the word ROTE under the title.

Music Reading: 149 songs; review of known elements; introduction of dotted quarter and eighth notes; easy chromatics; beginning of two-part singing.

All the songs correlate with the child's studies, interests, and experience.

Reproductions of Noted Pictures: Boy and Angel, *Abbott Thayer*, frontispiece; Boyhood of Raleigh, *Sir John E. Millais*, 19; Behind the Bamboo Screen, *James R. Hopkins*, 38; Venetian Waters, *Ettore Tito*, 55; Dutch Interior, *Pieter de Hooch*, 106; The Pipers of Balmoral, *Gari Melchers*, 123; The Haymakers, *Theodore C. Steele*, 142; The Harp of the Winds, *Homer D. Martin*, 159.

SONGS OF MANY LANDS

Let's Be Merry

ROTE

Rose Fyleman

Belgian Folk Tune

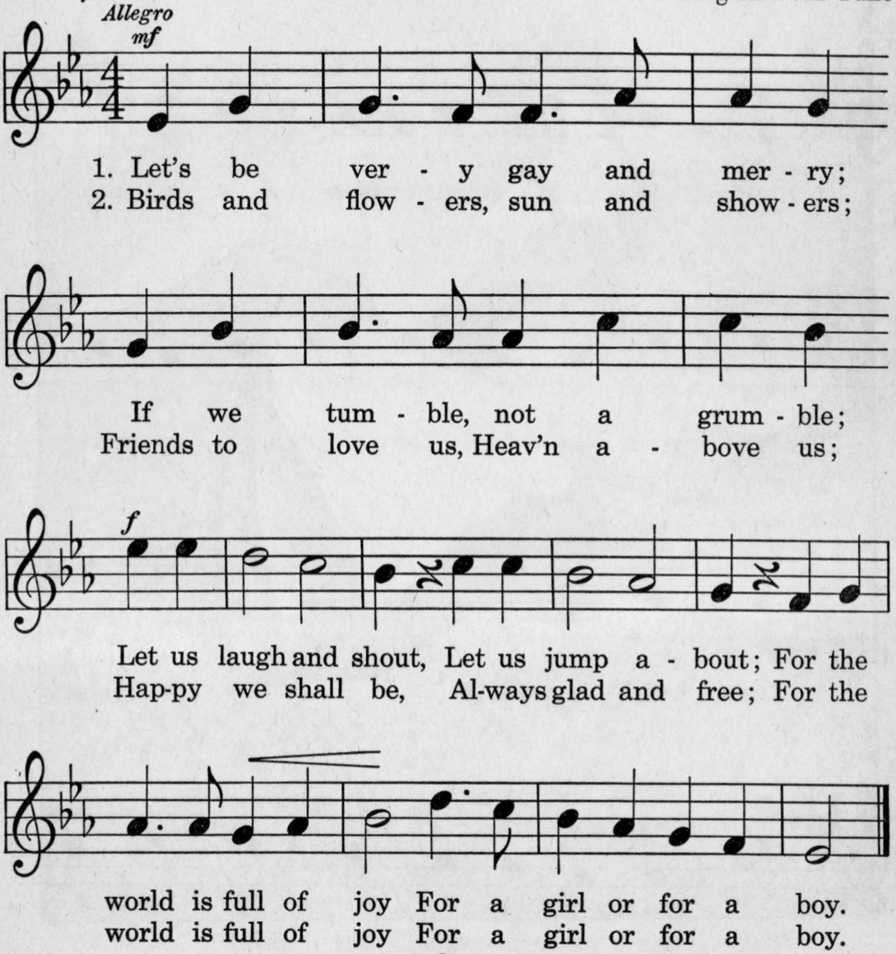
Allegro
mf
1. Let's be ver - y gay and mer - ry;
2. Birds and flow - ers, sun and show - ers;
If we tum - ble, not a grum - ble;
Friends to love us, Heav'n a - bove us;
f
Let us laugh and shout, Let us jump a - bout; For the
Hap-py we shall be, Al-ways glad and free; For the
world is full of joy For a girl or for a boy.
world is full of joy For a girl or for a boy.

The Merry-go-round

Susanna Myers | ROTE | Belgian Folk Tune

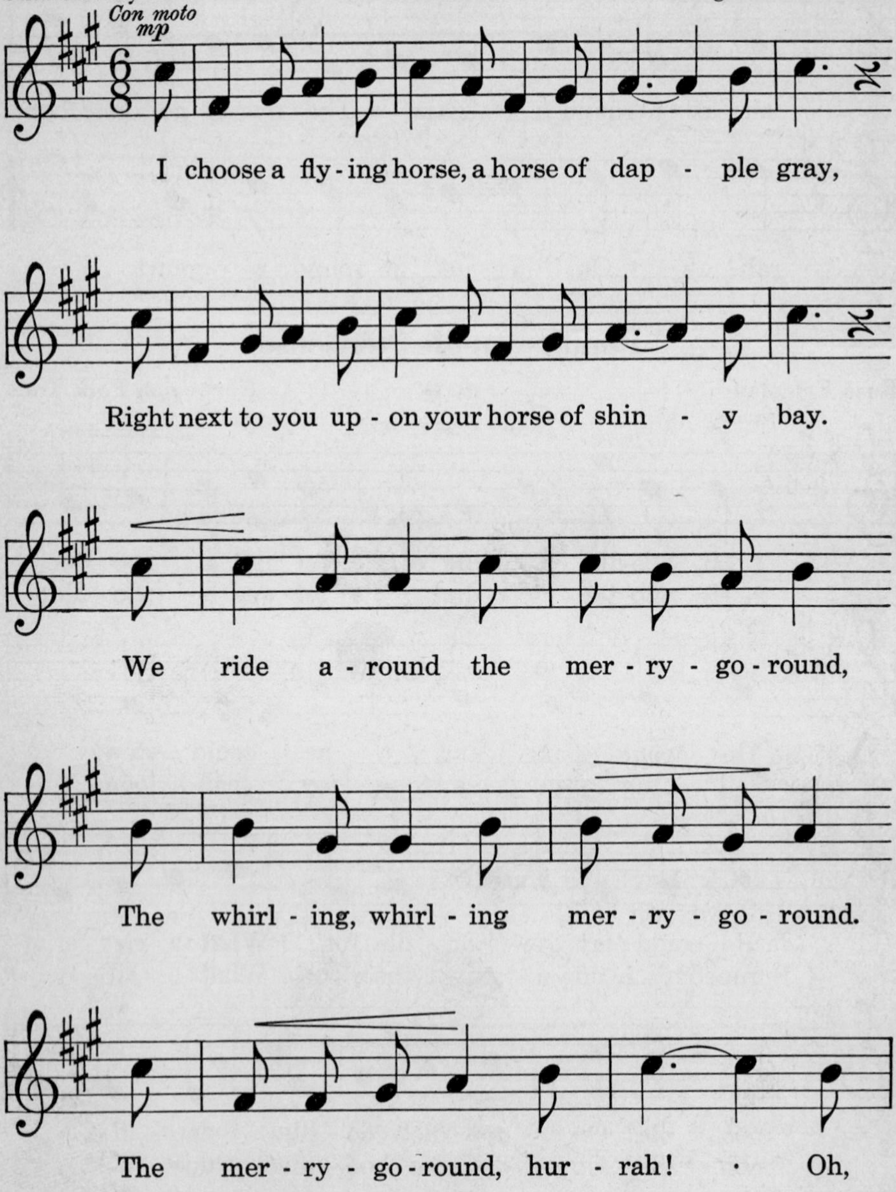
Con moto
mp
I choose a fly - ing horse, a horse of dap - ple gray,
Right next to you up - on your horse of shin - y bay.
We ride a - round the mer - ry - go - round,
The whirl - ing, whirl - ing mer - ry - go - round.
The mer - ry - go - round, hur - rah! Oh,

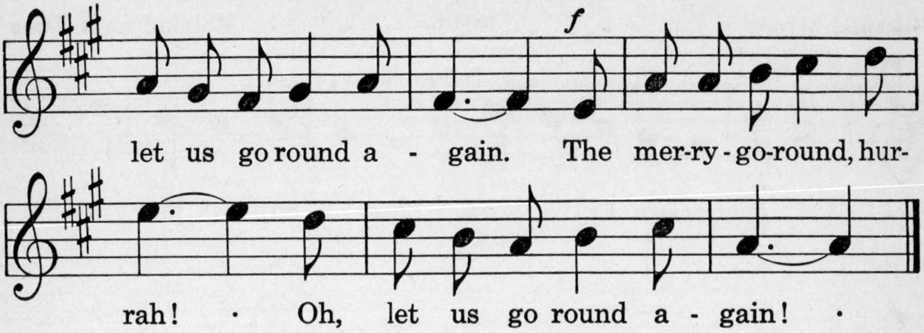
f
let us go round a - gain. The mer-ry - go-round, hur-
rah! · Oh, let us go round a - gain! ·

Poodle-Noodle Nonsense

Rose Fyleman | ROTE | Norwegian Folk Tune

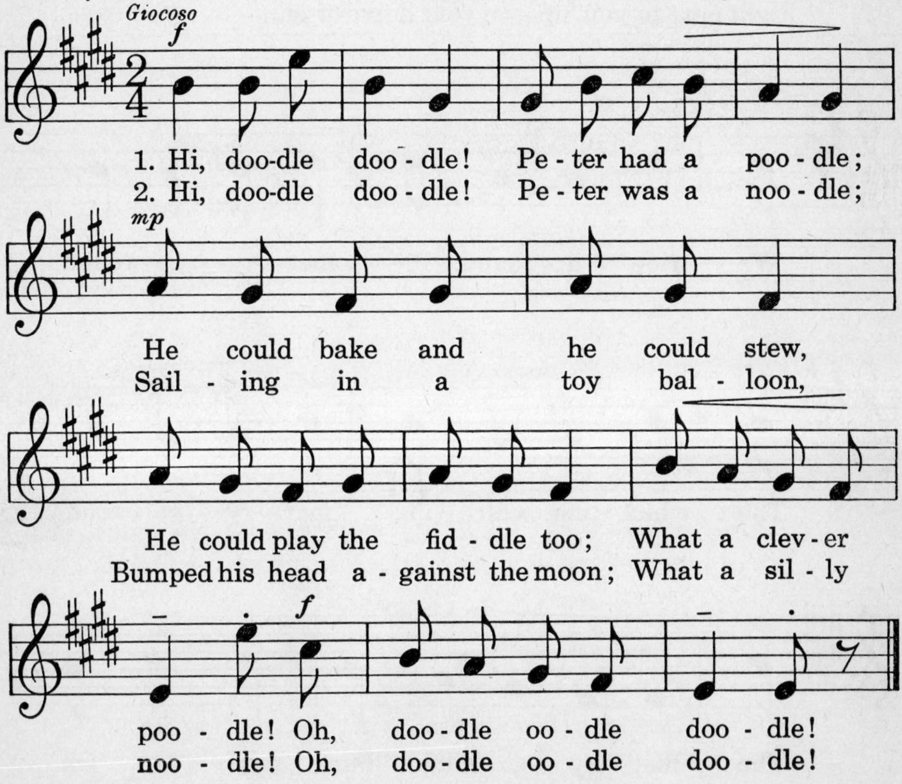
Giocoso
f
1. Hi, doo-dle doo - dle! Pe - ter had a poo - dle;
2. Hi, doo-dle doo - dle! Pe - ter was a noo - dle;
mp
He could bake and he could stew,
Sail - ing in a toy bal - loon,
He could play the fid - dle too; What a clev - er
Bumped his head a - gainst the moon; What a sil - ly
f
poo - dle! Oh, doo - dle oo - dle doo - dle!
noo - dle! Oh, doo - dle oo - dle doo - dle!

If I Had Wings

Christine Turner Curtis | ROTE | Lily Strickland

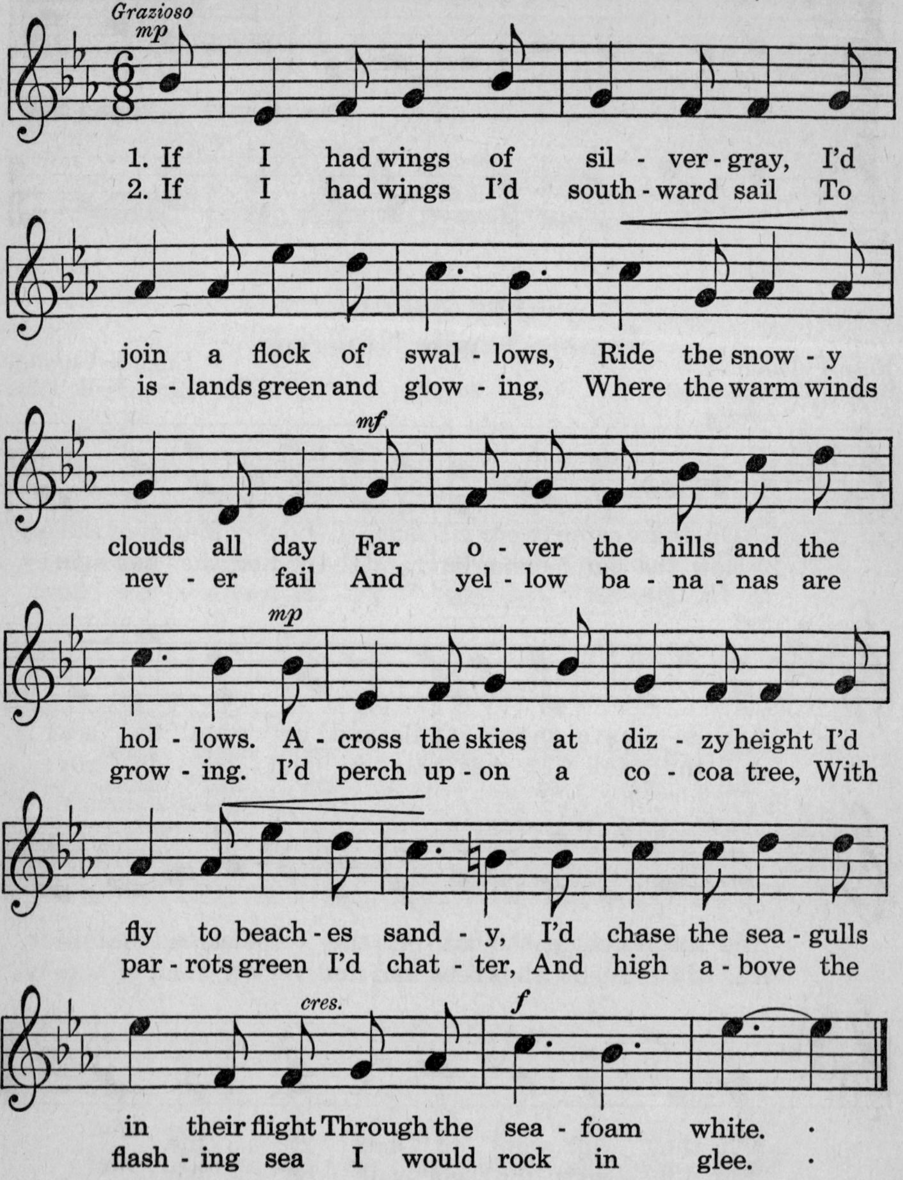
Grazioso
mp
1. If I had wings of sil - ver - gray, I'd
2. If I had wings I'd south - ward sail To
join a flock of swal - lows, Ride the snow - y
is - lands green and glow - ing, Where the warm winds
mf
clouds all day Far o - ver the hills and the
nev - er fail And yel - low ba - na - nas are
mp
hol - lows. A - cross the skies at diz - zy height I'd
grow - ing. I'd perch up - on a co - coa tree, With
fly to beach - es sand - y, I'd chase the sea - gulls
par - rots green I'd chat - ter, And high a - bove the
cres.
f
in their flight Through the sea - foam white.
flash - ing sea I would rock in glee.

The Sailor

ROTE

Rose Fyleman | English Chantey

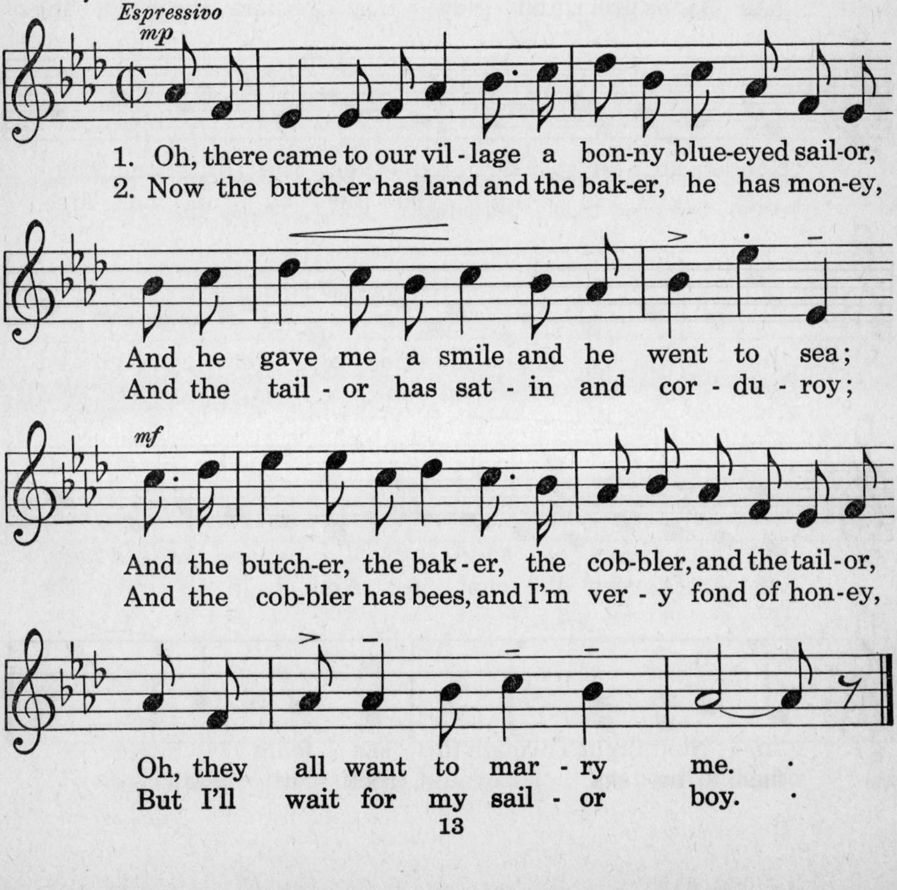
Espressivo
mp
1. Oh, there came to our vil-lage a bon-ny blue-eyed sail-or,
2. Now the butch-er has land and the bak-er, he has mon-ey,
And he gave me a smile and he went to sea;
And the tail - or has sat - in and cor - du - roy;
mf
And the butch-er, the bak-er, the cob-bler, and the tail-or,
And the cob-bler has bees, and I'm ver - y fond of hon-ey,
Oh, they all want to mar - ry me.
But I'll wait for my sail - or boy.

The Woodcutter

Luther Wilde — ROTE — Frances McCollin

Allegretto
mf
1. Through the lone - ly for - est tracks Goes the wood-man with his ax; He is al - ways chop-ping, He sends the splin-ters hop-ping. His eyes are clear as sum-mer rain, He chops a - way with might and main.
2. When the sun is o - ver - head Then the wood-man eats his bread. By the brook-let flow - ing He hears the pine tree blow-ing. He sees the tim - id squir-rels run, He has a crumb for ev - 'ry - one.
cres.
f
leggiero
Tra la la la, tra la la la, tra la la la la, He
Tra la la la, tra la la la, tra la la la la, He
1
sings in mer - ry vein.
2
cres.
f
greets the noon-day sun.

The Little Farmer

American Traditional — ROTE — American Traditional

Semplice
mf
1. Once there lived a lit - tle man where a
2. Once his lit - tle maid - en Ann with her
3. Such a clat - ter now be - gan as a -
4. Then, to make the sto - ry short, lit - tle
lit - tle riv - er ran, And he had a lit - tle
pret - ty milk - ing can Went a - milk - ing when the
larmed the lit - tle man, Who came ca - per - ing from
po - ny with a snort Lift - ed up his lit - tle
farm and lit - tle dai - ry - o: Oh, he had a lit- tle
morn-ing sun was beam-ing - o; And she fell, I don't know
out his lit - tle sta - ble - o; Po-ny stepped on dog - gie's
heels so ver - y clev - er - o; And the man came tum-bling
plow, lit - tle po - ny, lit - tle cow, And a
how, but she stum - bled o'er the plow, And the
toes, dog - gie snapped at po - ny's nose, Pig - gie
down and he al - most cracked his crown, But this
pig - gie and a dog he called his Ter - ry - o.
cow was quite as - ton-ished at her scream-ing - o.
made as loud a noise as he was a - ble - o.
on - ly made the mat - ter worse than ev - er - o.

Playing Cowboys

Mary C. Gleitz

Polish Folk Tune

Ben marcato
mf
1. If you would be brave in - deed,
2. See them, see them! There they go!
3. Whoa, now! whoa, now! Hold them still!
Fol - low, fol - low where I lead.
Herds of dust - y buf - fa - lo.
See that lit - tle rock - y hill!
Watch me when my rope I swing
Hold - ing tight our po - nies' reins,
Let your po - nies walk with care,
For I can las - so an - y - thing.
We gal - lop, gal - lop, o'er the plains.
For In - dians may be hid - ing there.

Below and Above

Marchette Gaylord Chute | Theo Halle

Moderato
mp
1. Warm, warm, un - der - ground
2. High, high, in the trees
Ti - ny crea - tures may be found;
Rob - ins sail on leaf - y seas.
Where the swal - lows nest in hol - lows,
There the sing - ing boats go wing - ing,
Where the bee - tles play a - round,
Go - ing an - y - where they please.
mf
Warm, warm, un - der - ground
High, high, in the trees
Ti - ny crea - tures may be found.
Rob - ins sail on leaf - y seas.

Louise Ayres Garnett — Czechoslovakian Folk Tune

Con anima
mf
1. Once I set out to dis - cov - er
2. Still I trav - eled on and on - ward;
Where the world ends,
Far did I go,
Down a riv - er, up a moun - tain,
O - ver riv - ers, o - ver moun - tains,
Where the sky bends.
Through the deep snow.
But the way, strange to say, Ran a - long night and day;
All the way, day by day, Did not stop, did not play,

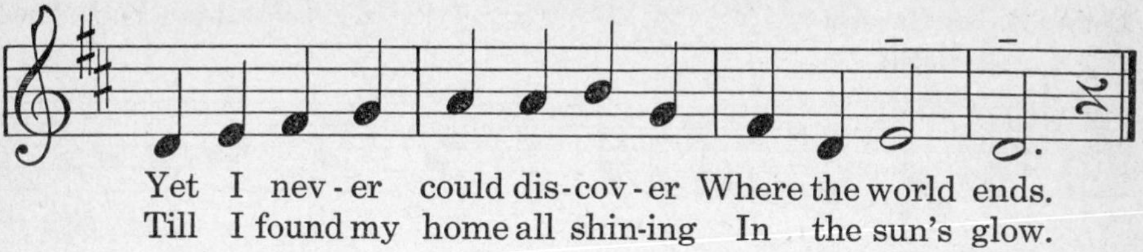
Yet I nev - er could dis-cov - er Where the world ends.
Till I found my home all shin-ing In the sun's glow.

The Art Extension Press, Inc.

Boyhood of Raleigh

Painted by the English artist JOHN E. MILLAIS
in 1870. It is in the Tate Gallery, London

Autumn Wind

Christine Turner Curtis — ROTE — Margaret K. Fowler

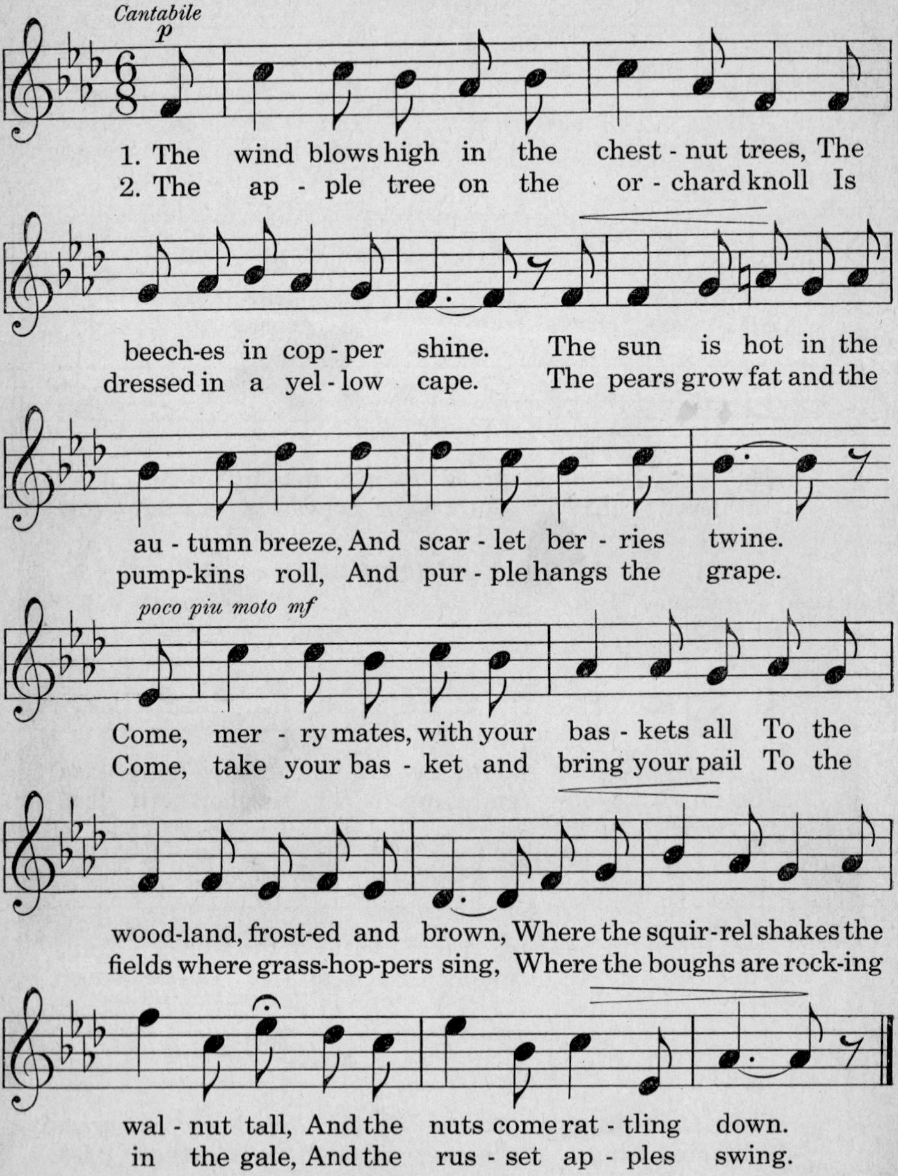
Cantabile
p
1. The wind blows high in the chest - nut trees, The
2. The ap - ple tree on the or - chard knoll Is
beech-es in cop - per shine. The sun is hot in the
dressed in a yel - low cape. The pears grow fat and the
au - tumn breeze, And scar - let ber - ries twine.
pump-kins roll, And pur - ple hangs the grape.
poco piu moto mf
Come, mer - ry mates, with your bas - kets all To the
Come, take your bas - ket and bring your pail To the
wood-land, frost-ed and brown, Where the squir-rel shakes the
fields where grass-hop-pers sing, Where the boughs are rock-ing
wal - nut tall, And the nuts come rat - tling down.
in the gale, And the rus - set ap - ples swing.

The Scarecrow

Lois Lenski — Polish Folk Tune

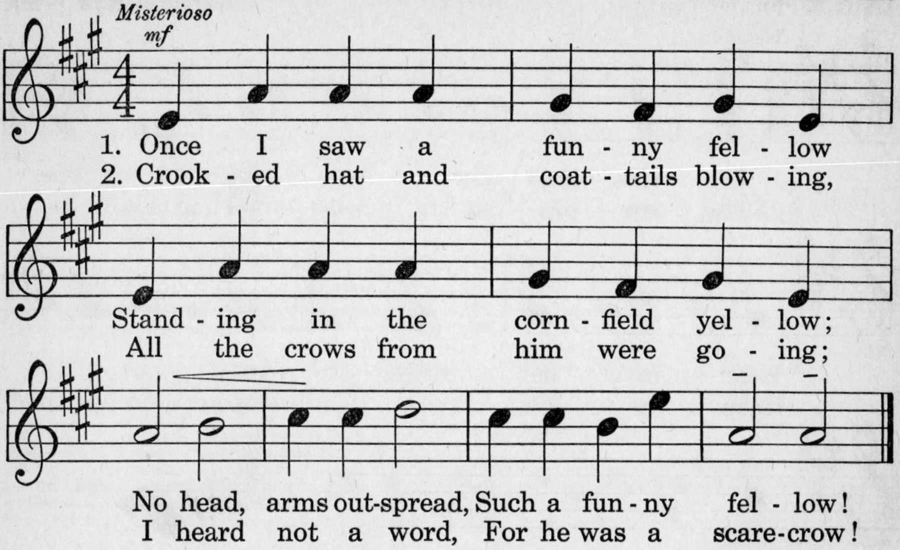
Misterioso
mf
1. Once I saw a fun - ny fel - low
2. Crook - ed hat and coat - tails blow - ing,
Stand - ing in the corn - field yel - low;
All the crows from him were go - ing;
No head, arms out-spread, Such a fun - ny fel - low!
I heard not a word, For he was a scare-crow!

At the Pasture Bars

Translated by Susanna Myers — French Folk Song

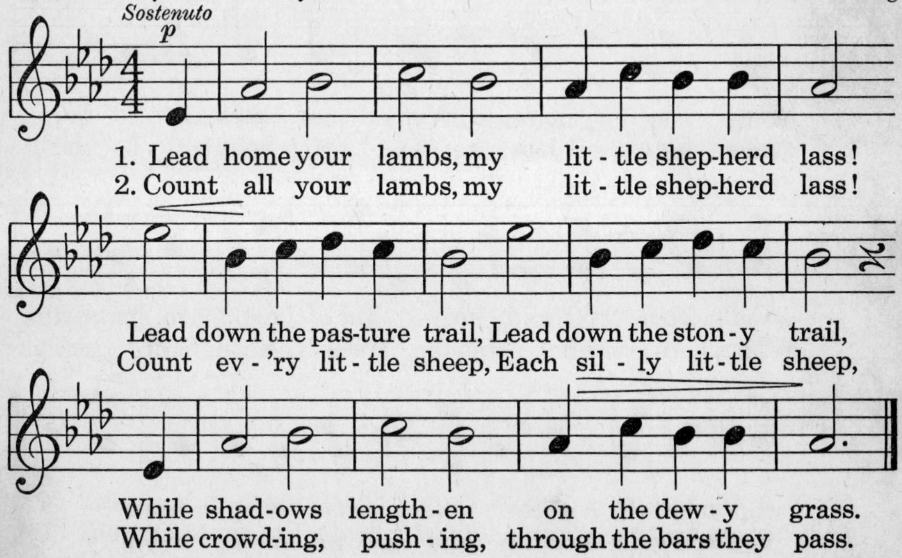
Sostenuto
p
1. Lead home your lambs, my lit - tle shep-herd lass!
2. Count all your lambs, my lit - tle shep-herd lass!
Lead down the pas-ture trail, Lead down the ston - y trail,
Count ev - 'ry lit - tle sheep, Each sil - ly lit - tle sheep,
While shad-ows length - en on the dew - y grass.
While crowd-ing, push - ing, through the bars they pass.

Boasting

Clara Louise Kessler

Hungarian Folk Tune

Giocoso
p
1. "Lis - ten," says the man - do - lin,
2. Trum - pet now as loud - ly shrills,
"Hear my tin - kling tune."
Harp be - gins to hum.
mp
"Hear me," sings the vi - o - lin,
Fair - y flute then sweet - ly trills,
With a gen - tle croon.
Horn blares "tum - ti - tum."
mf
"O - boe, trom - bone, pic - co - lo,
"What is all this fuss a - bout?
I am best of all you know," boasts the deep bas-soon.
I am best be - yond a doubt," beats the big bass drum.

Golden September

Ethel Crowninshield

Robert W. Gibb

Grazioso
mf
1. In gold-en Sep - tem-ber with bright sun-ny days,
2. I love the green May-time, the white win-ter snow;
The skies are clear and blue. . .
I love the sum - mer too. . .
The bee's in the clo-ver, al - though sum-mer's o - ver.
But gold-en Sep - tem-ber I al - ways re - mem-ber,
f
p
I love Sep - tem - ber, don't you? Don't you?
I can't tell why, but I do, I do!
mf
I love Sep - tem - ber, don't you? . .
I can't tell why, but I do! . .

Jack-o'-lantern

Virginia Lynd Hartley

Swedish Folk Tune

Allegretto
mp
Wait till the sky is dark,
Then bring the pump - kin round,
When cats are still and no dogs bark!
That frost has mel - lowed on the ground.
mf
Cut big eyes and then a nose,
Next a mouth with teeth in rows.
Oh, oh, spook - y sight,
Jack - o' - lan - tern in the night.

Mowing the Barley

ROTE

Adapted from the original — English Folk Song

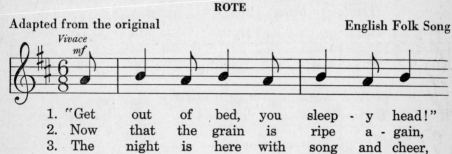

Vivace

1. "Get out of bed, you sleep - y head!"
2. Now that the grain is ripe a - gain,
3. The night is here with song and cheer,

Cries Fa - ther to young Mar - ley.
We can - not stop to par - ley.
Come, Pe - ter, Bess, and Char - lie:

"It's break of day, we must a - way;
But quick and blithe, with stone and scythe,
We'll dance at last, for work is past,

"It's time to mow the bar - ley."
We keep on mow - ing bar - ley.
And we have mowed the bar - ley.

Our Trip

Rebecca Foresman — Dutch Folk Tune

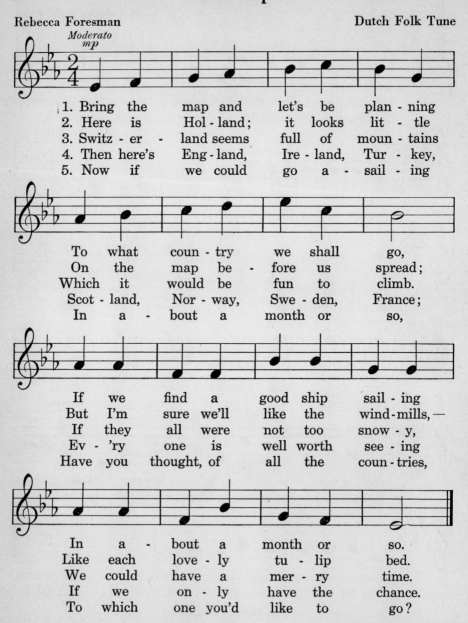

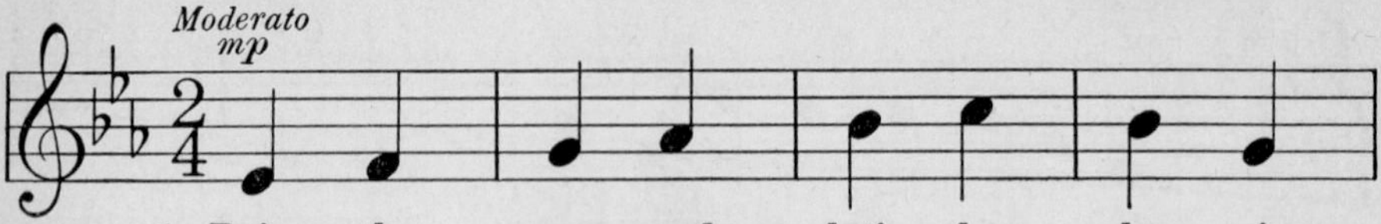

1. Bring the map and let's be plan - ning
2. Here is Hol - land; it looks lit - tle
3. Switz - er - land seems full of moun - tains
4. Then here's Eng - land, Ire - land, Tur - key,
5. Now if we could go a - sail - ing

To what coun - try we shall go,
On the map be - fore us spread;
Which it would be fun to climb.
Scot - land, Nor - way, Swe - den, France;
In a - bout a month or so,

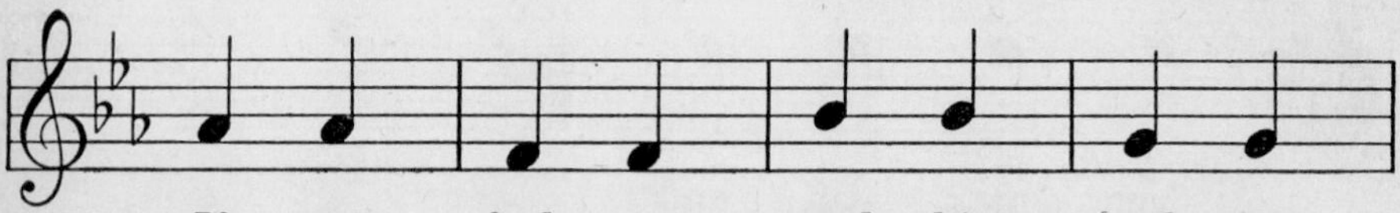

If we find a good ship sail - ing
But I'm sure we'll like the wind-mills, —
If they all were not too snow - y,
Ev - 'ry one is well worth see - ing
Have you thought, of all the coun - tries,

In a - bout a month or so.
Like each love - ly tu - lip bed.
We could have a mer - ry time.
If we on - ly have the chance.
To which one you'd like to go?

A Queer Business

Rose Fyleman

Bohemian Folk Tune

Giojoso
mf
1. In the for-est, when the moon is bright, (wump, wump, wump.)[1]
2. In the field be-tween the cab-bage rows, (hush, hush, hush.)
All the bears are danc-ing in its light. (thump, thump, thump.)
All the mice are danc-ing on their toes. (tush, tush, tush.)
In a sol - emn ring they go,
If the cat should chance to roam,
Ver - y stiff and ver - y slow,
They would all go scam - p'ring home,
Sing-ing with a bear-ish sort of sound, (grump, grump, grump.)
To their holes they'd scam-per in a trice; (rush, rush, rush.)
p meno mosso
pp
While they cir -cle round and round and round. (wump, wump, wump.)
Pray be ver - y wa - ry, lit-tle mice. (hush, hush, hush.)

[1]May be sung or spoken.

The Flower Girl

Cecil Cowdrey

Italian Folk Tune

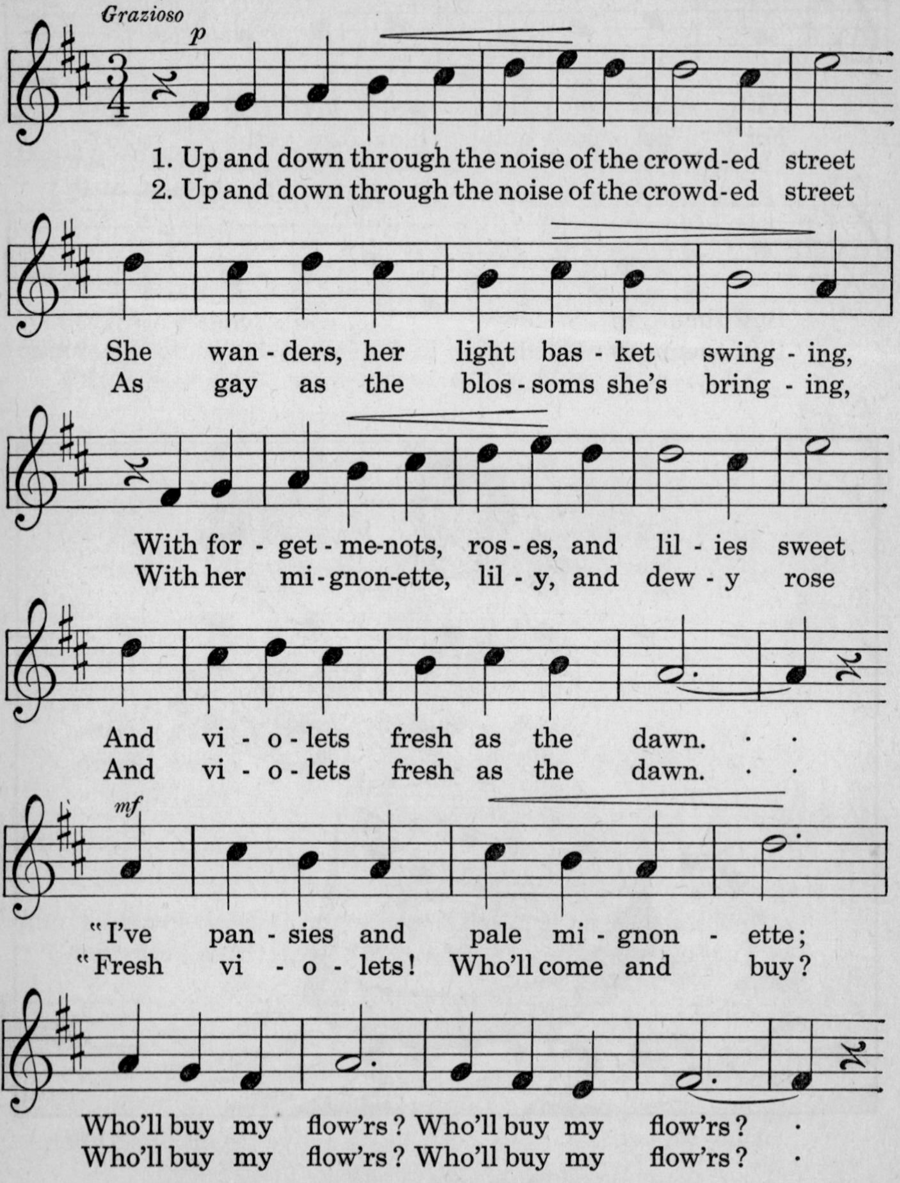
Grazioso
p
1. Up and down through the noise of the crowd-ed street
2. Up and down through the noise of the crowd-ed street
She wan - ders, her light bas - ket swing - ing,
As gay as the blos - soms she's bring - ing,
With for - get - me-nots, ros - es, and lil - ies sweet
With her mi - gnon-ette, lil - y, and dew - y rose
And vi - o - lets fresh as the dawn.
And vi - o - lets fresh as the dawn.
mf
"I've pan - sies and pale mi - gnon - ette;
"Fresh vi - o - lets! Who'll come and buy?
Who'll buy my flow'rs? Who'll buy my flow'rs?
Who'll buy my flow'rs? Who'll buy my flow'rs?

With dew of the val - ley still wet;
For - get - me - nots blue as the sky!
Buy them to - day. Buy while you may!"
Buy them to - day. Buy while you may!"

Singing, We Go

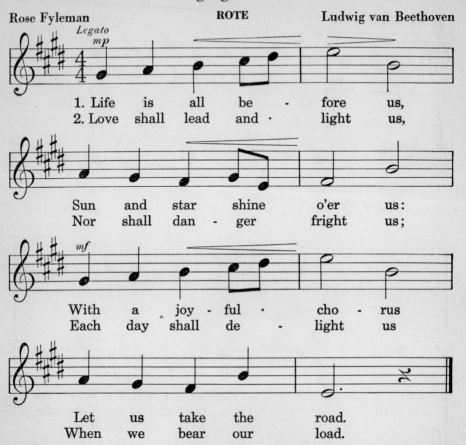

Rose Fyleman — ROTE — Ludwig van Beethoven

1. Life is all be - fore us,
2. Love shall lead and · light us,

Sun and star shine o'er us:
Nor shall dan - ger fright us;

With a joy - ful · cho - rus
Each day shall de - light us

Let us take the road.
When we bear our load.

A Houseful

Marjorie Knapp — ROTE — Helen T. Witherow

1. A lit - tle old la - dy, who lived all a - lone, Cried,
2. A doz - en good neigh-bors, who wished to be kind, All

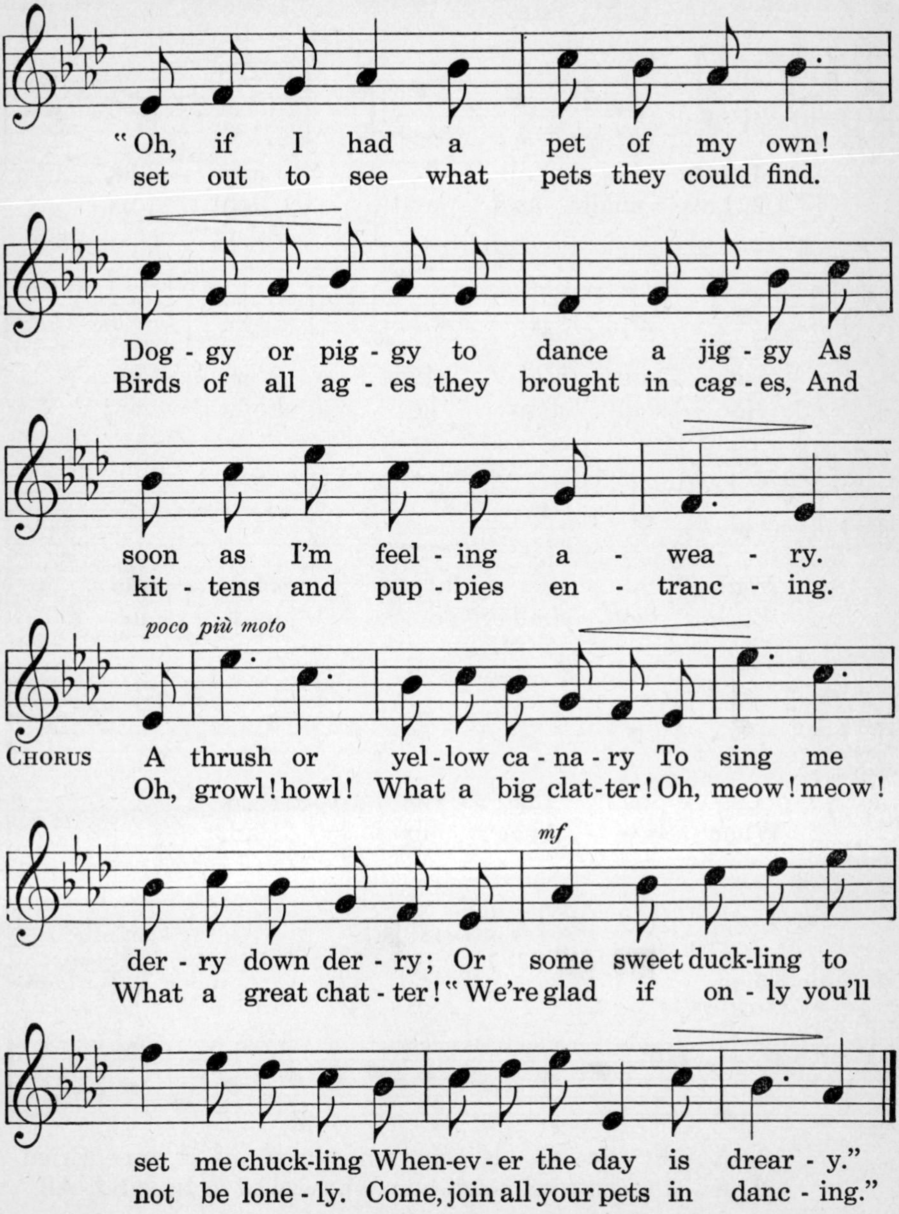
"Oh, if I had a pet of my own!
set out to see what pets they could find.
Dog - gy or pig - gy to dance a jig - gy As
Birds of all ag - es they brought in cag - es, And
soon as I'm feel - ing a - wea - ry.
kit - tens and pup - pies en - tranc - ing.
poco più moto
Chorus
A thrush or yel - low ca - na - ry To sing me
Oh, growl! howl! What a big clat - ter! Oh, meow! meow!
mf
der - ry down der - ry; Or some sweet duck-ling to
What a great chat - ter! "We're glad if on - ly you'll
set me chuck-ling When-ev - er the day is drear - y."
not be lone - ly. Come, join all your pets in danc - ing."

An Old Garden

Margaret Widdemer | Basque Folk Tune

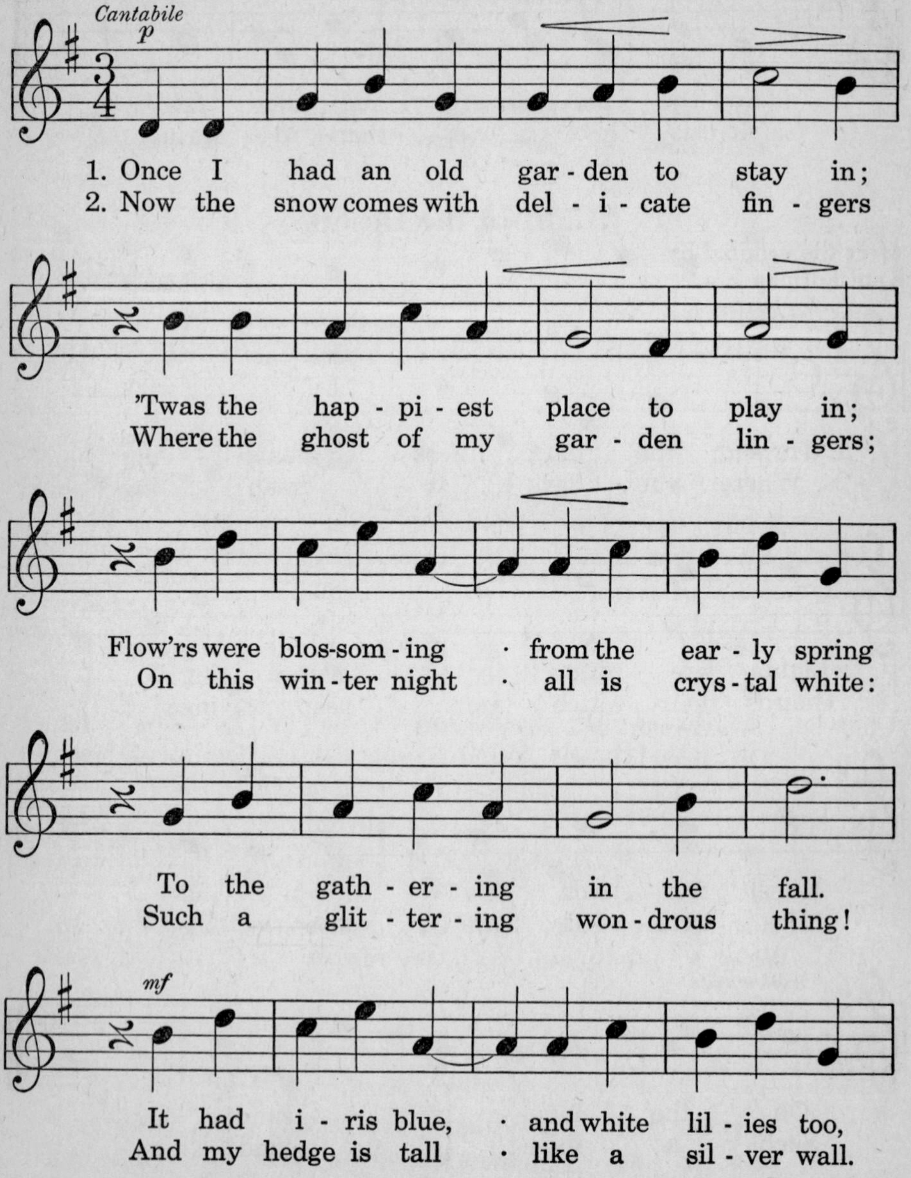
Cantabile
p
1. Once I had an old gar - den to stay in;
2. Now the snow comes with del - i - cate fin - gers
'Twas the hap - pi - est place to play in;
Where the ghost of my gar - den lin - gers;
Flow'rs were blos-som - ing · from the ear - ly spring
On this win - ter night · all is crys - tal white:
To the gath - er - ing in the fall.
Such a glit - ter - ing won - drous thing!
mf
It had i - ris blue, · and white lil - ies too,
And my hedge is tall · like a sil - ver wall.

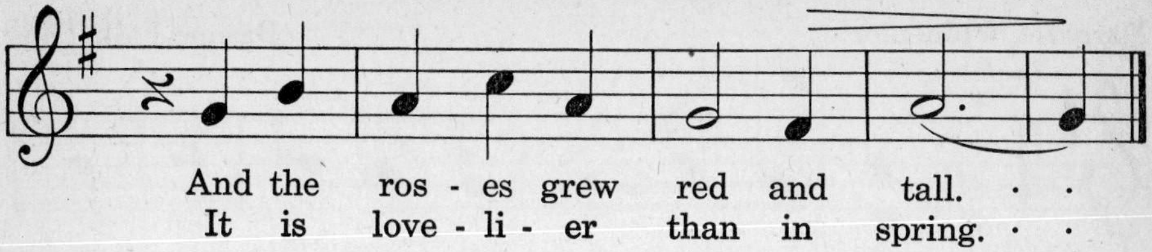
And the ros - es grew red and tall. . .
It is love - li - er than in spring. . .

Night in the Desert

After the original by
Kate Forman

Arabian Folk Song

Espressivo
p
1. Through the dark - ness gleam - ing
2. Where the dark is creep - ing
Lights are dim - ly beam - ing;
Guards their watch are keep - ing;
Kneel - ing cam - els dream - ing
Des - ert folk are sleep - ing;
rallentando
On the lone - ly sand.
Such a lone - ly land!

What Will You Do?

Susanna Myers

French-Canadian Folk Tune

Cantabile
mp
1. What will you do? What will you be
2. Will you be brave? Will you be bold
When you are old - er, wise and free?
Like the ex - plor - ers famed of old?
mf
How would you like to wan - der far
Gal - lant, cou - ra - geous, firm and true
By sea and land and air? Will you ex -
To fol - low roads that wind? Will you ex -
plore the wide, wide world, Its won-ders to share?
plore the wide, wide world, Its se - crets to find?

Singing

Susanna Myers — Swedish Folk Tune

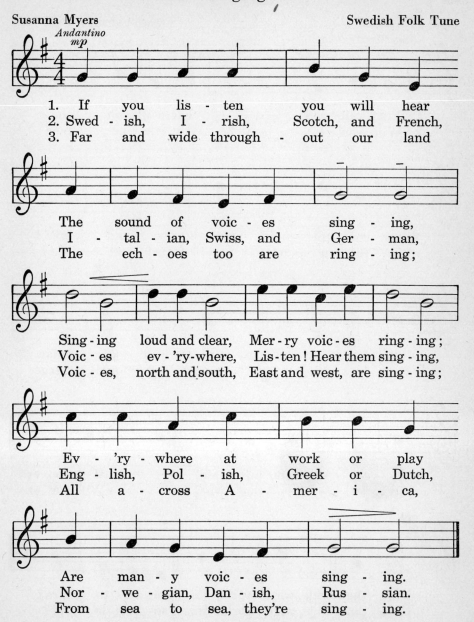

1. If you lis - ten you will hear
2. Swed - ish, I - rish, Scotch, and French,
3. Far and wide through - out our land

The sound of voic - es sing - ing,
I - tal - ian, Swiss, and Ger - man,
The ech - oes too are ring - ing;

Sing - ing loud and clear, Mer - ry voic - es ring - ing;
Voic - es ev - 'ry-where, Lis - ten! Hear them sing - ing,
Voic - es, north and south, East and west, are sing - ing;

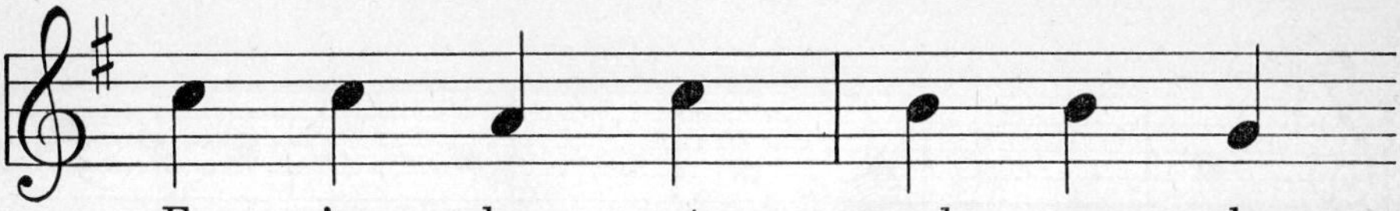

Ev - 'ry - where at work or play
Eng - lish, Pol - ish, Greek or Dutch,
All a - cross A - mer - i - ca,

Are man - y voic - es sing - ing.
Nor - we - gian, Dan - ish, Rus - sian.
From sea to sea, they're sing - ing.

A Summer Picture

Ethel Crowninshield — Chinese Folk Tune

Dolce cantabile

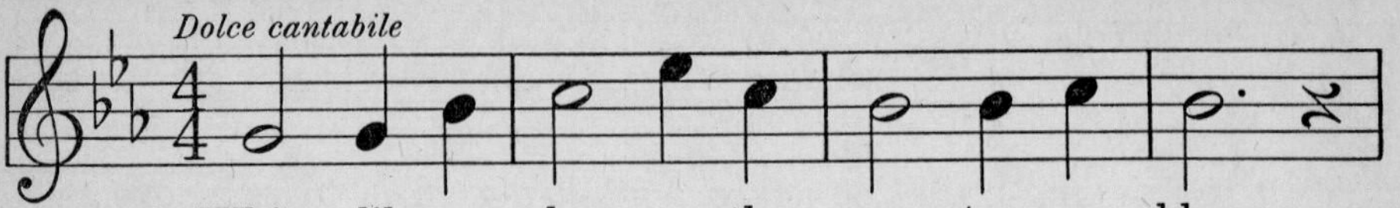

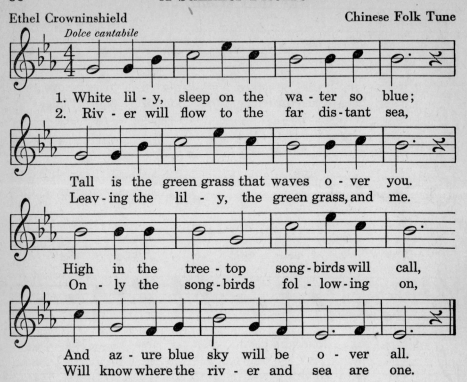

1. White lil - y, sleep on the wa - ter so blue;
2. Riv - er will flow to the far dis - tant sea,

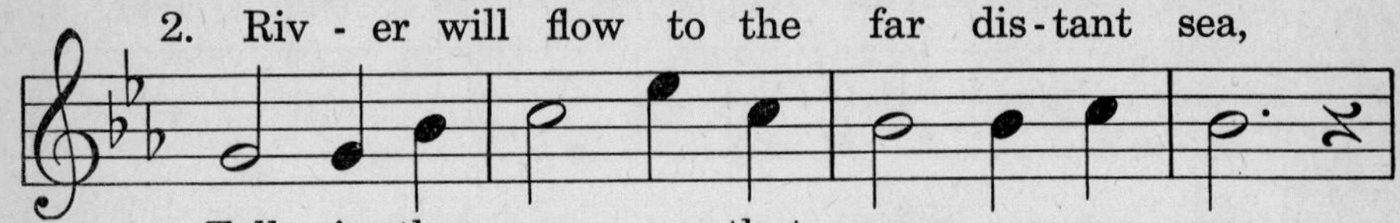

Tall is the green grass that waves o - ver you.
Leav - ing the lil - y, the green grass, and me.

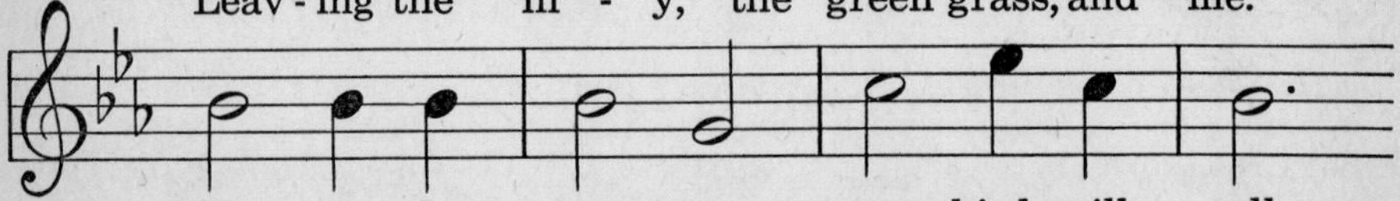

High in the tree - top song - birds will call,
On - ly the song - birds fol - low - ing on,

And az - ure blue sky will be o - ver all.
Will know where the riv - er and sea are one.

Sunny Italy

Christine Turner Curtis — ROTE — Gaetano Donizetti

Con grazia

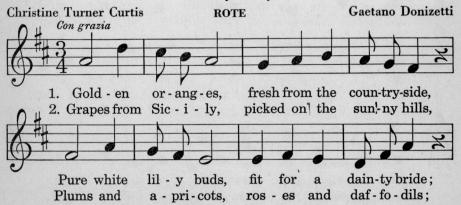

1. Gold - en or - ang - es, fresh from the coun-try-side,
2. Grapes from Sic - i - ly, picked on the sun - ny hills,

Pure white lil - y buds, fit for a dain-ty bride;
Plums and a - pri - cots, ros - es and daf - fo - dils;

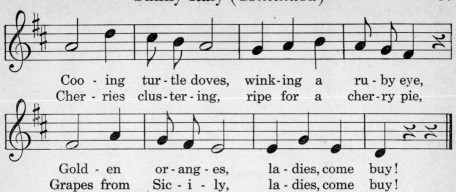

Coo - ing tur - tle doves, wink-ing a ru - by eye,
Cher - ries clus - ter - ing, ripe for a cher - ry pie,

Gold - en or - ang - es, la - dies, come buy!
Grapes from Sic - i - ly, la - dies, come buy!

The Smiling Little Lass

Ethel Crowninshield | ROTE | Irish Folk Tune

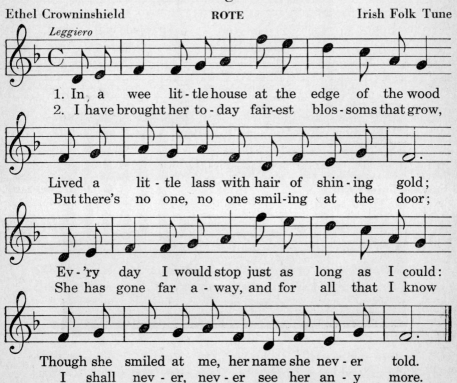

1. In a wee lit - tle house at the edge of the wood
2. I have brought her to - day fair-est blos - soms that grow,

Lived a lit - tle lass with hair of shin - ing gold;
But there's no one, no one smil-ing at the door;

Ev - 'ry day I would stop just as long as I could:
She has gone far a - way, and for all that I know

Though she smiled at me, her name she nev - er told.
I shall nev - er, nev - er see her an - y more.

The Art Extension Press, Inc.

Behind the Bamboo Screen

Painted by the American artist James R. Hopkins

The Bamboo Screen

English version by
Christine Turner Curtis

ROTE

Japanese Folk Song

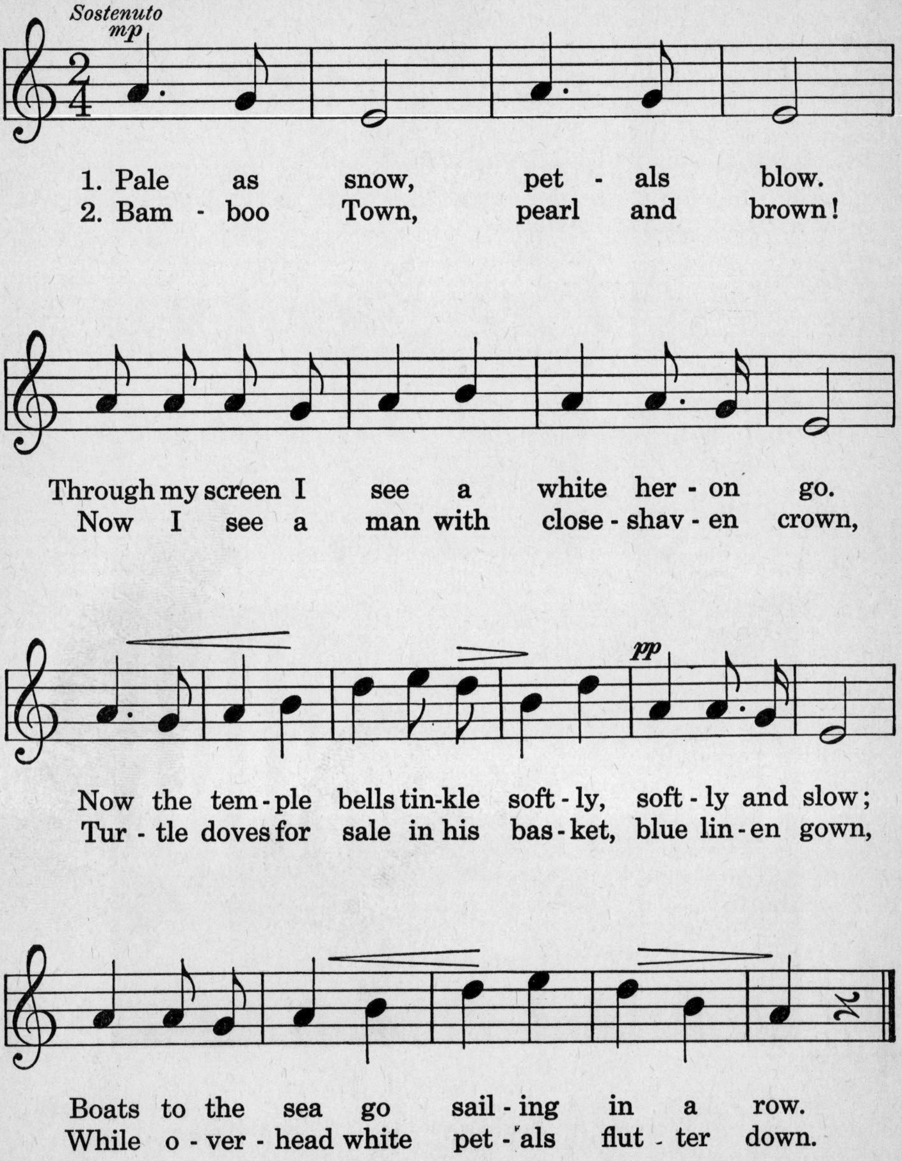
Sostenuto
mp
1. Pale as snow, pet - als blow.
2. Bam - boo Town, pearl and brown!
Through my screen I see a white her - on go.
Now I see a man with close - shav - en crown,
pp
Now the tem - ple bells tin-kle soft - ly, soft - ly and slow;
Tur - tle doves for sale in his bas - ket, blue lin - en gown,
Boats to the sea go sail - ing in a row.
While o - ver - head white pet - als flut - ter down.

Living Out of Doors

English version by
Mary C. Gleitz

Hungarian Folk Song

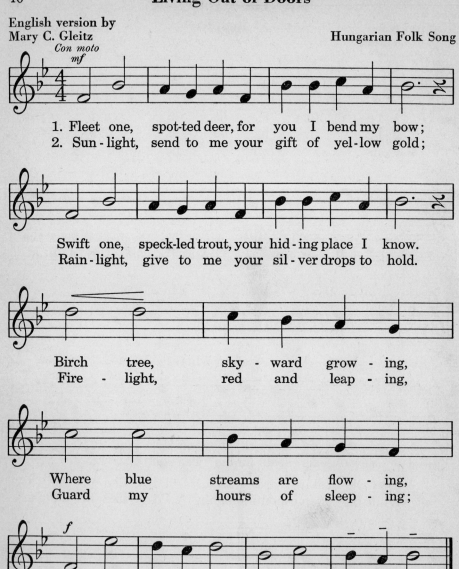

1. Fleet one, spot-ted deer, for you I bend my bow;
2. Sun - light, send to me your gift of yel-low gold;

Swift one, speck-led trout, your hid - ing place I know.
Rain - light, give to me your sil - ver drops to hold.

Birch tree, sky - ward grow - ing,
Fire - light, red and leap - ing,

Where blue streams are flow - ing,
Guard my hours of sleep - ing;

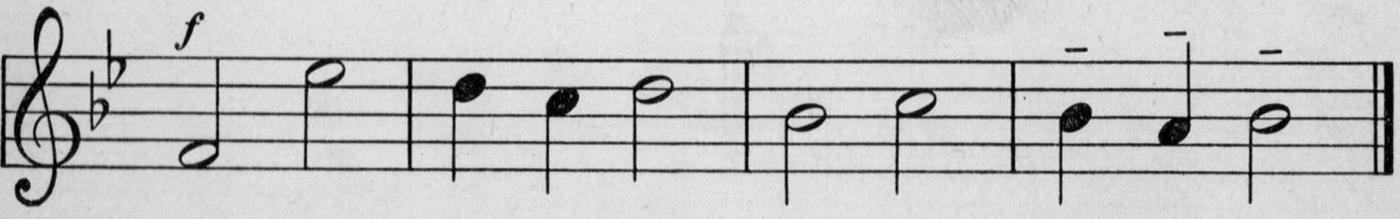

I have need of you For my small ca - noe!
Be my broth - er bright, Be my friend at night!

The Gypsy

Carol Fuller

Spanish Folk Tune

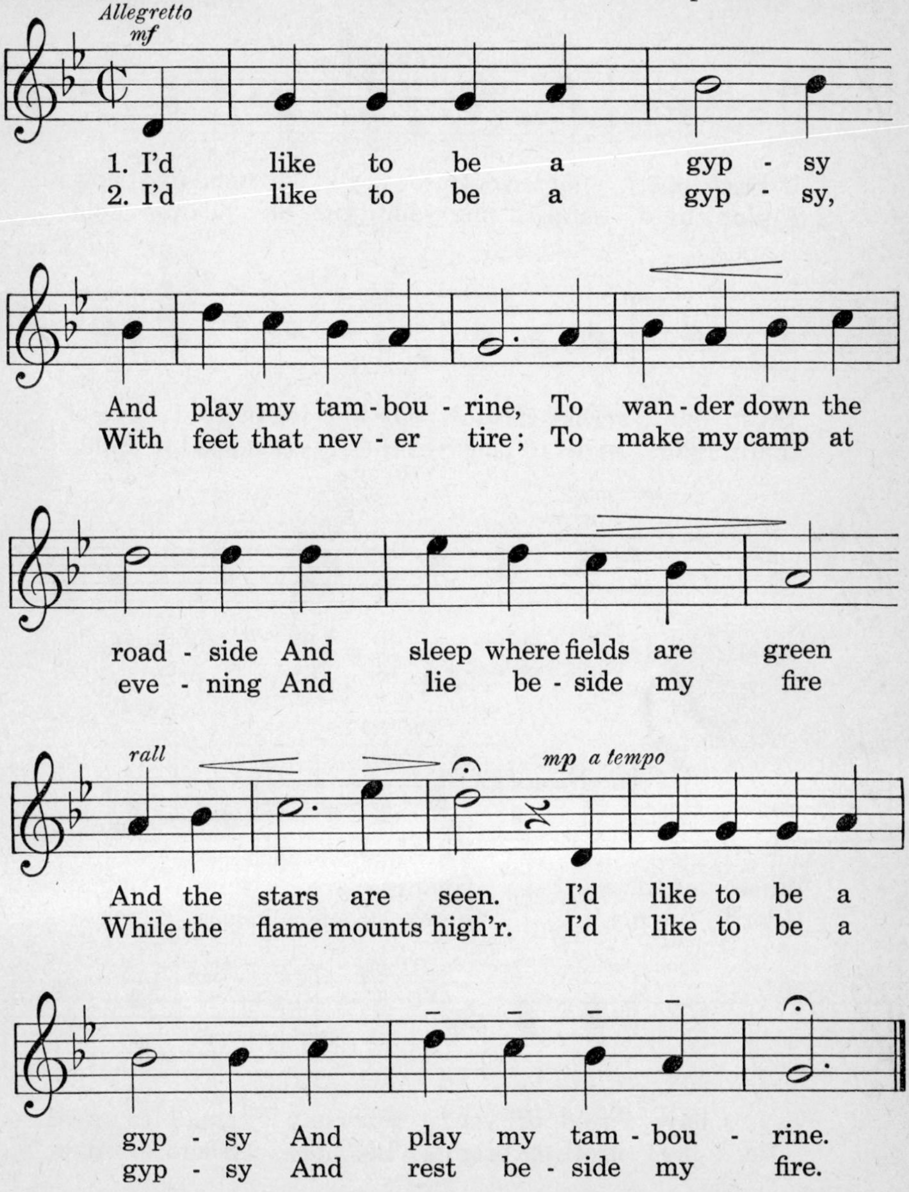
Allegretto
mf
1. I'd like to be a gyp - sy
2. I'd like to be a gyp - sy,
And play my tam - bou - rine, To wan - der down the
With feet that nev - er tire; To make my camp at
road - side And sleep where fields are green
eve - ning And lie be - side my fire
rall
mp a tempo
And the stars are seen. I'd like to be a
While the flame mounts high'r. I'd like to be a
gyp - sy And play my tam - bou - rine.
gyp - sy And rest be - side my fire.

Sung at Harvest Time

English version by
Christine Turner Curtis

ROTE

Inca Melody

Dolce espressivo
mp
1. Come, my sis - ters, come, my broth - ers,
2. Praise to thee, O might - y In - ti,[1]
At the sound-ing of the horn; . .
For the bar - ley and the cane! . .
On the hill - sides, on the moun-tains,
In the wheat fields, in the corn fields,
Har - vest we the yel - low corn. . .
Har - vest we the yel - low grain. . .
mf
Gold - en shines our Fa - ther Sun; . .
Soft - ly blows the au - tumn wind; . .

[1] Pronounced "In-tē" and means 'sun god.'

p
Sil - ver shines our Moth - er Moon; · ·
Gen - tly wave the silk - en leaves; · ·
mp
Sick - les flash - ing, fill your bas - kets,
Reap - ers sing - ing, press we on - ward,
rallentando
Reap - ing in the yel - low noon. · ·
Ty - ing up the yel - low sheaves. · ·

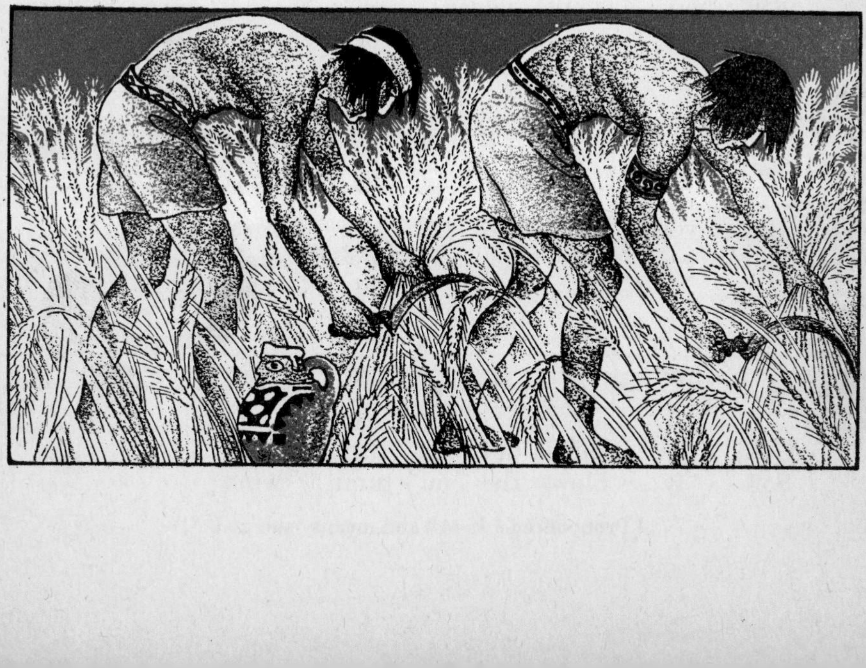

Suppose

Nellie Poorman

Austrian Folk Tune

Con anima
mf
1. Sup - pose that puss could laugh and shout
2. Sup - pose that ducks could read and write,
3. Sup - pose the leaf - y trees should go
While I could on - ly purr;
And el - e - phants wore shoes;
Pa - rad - ing down the street,
Sup - pose my dog wore coat and hat,
That hors - es sat by can - dle - light
And hol - ly - hocks danced to and fro
f
And I had heav - y fur. How ver - y queer the
To read the dai - ly news. A fun - ny cir - cus
While I had roots for feet. I should not wish that
world would seem! 'Twould be just like a dream.
that would be To come in dreams to me.
dream to last; I'd wake up ver - y fast.

Little Gobbelin

ROTE

Rose Fyleman

Danish Folk Tune

Semplice
mp
1. There was a lit - tle · gob - be - lin Who
2. This naugh - ty lit - tle · gob - be - lin, He
stayed at home all day, And did his bit of ·
grew so full of fun, That out he came a -
cob - be - lin' And nev - er went out to · play.
hob - be - lin' Be - fore the day's work was · done.
mf
Late at night when there was no light,
Old Witch Grim came right aft - er him,
Then out he would pop with a hop, hop, hop
All in, in and out and a - round a - bout;
p
And scare good folk a - way.
Oh, how he had to run!

The Friendly Toad

James Dyrenforth — Russian Folk Tune

Ben marcato
mf
1. Ev - 'ry lit - tle toad, 'tis said,
2. "Well," he said, "my eyes are bright
3. Now I know what toads are for,
Has two bright jew - els in his head;
Be - cause I have to see at night;
I'll nev - er chase them an - y more.
They are not the kind you buy, For
No mos - qui - to buzz - ing by Es -
Through the night a watch they keep And
f
each is just a shin - ing eye. Toad, toad, tell me, do!
capes my ev - er watch-ful eye. Come, come, come! I say,
catch mos-qui-toes while I sleep. Toad, toad, now I see
p
Why these gems were giv - en you. Toad, toad,
Please, mos - qui - to, come and play! Come, come,
Real - ly you're a friend to me. Toad, toad,

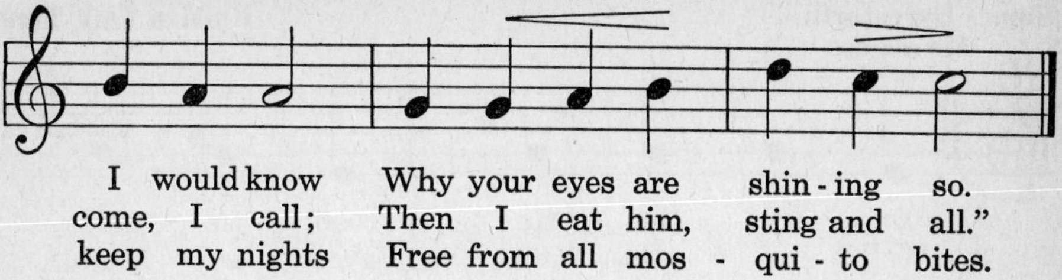
I would know Why your eyes are shin-ing so.
come, I call; Then I eat him, sting and all."
keep my nights Free from all mos-qui-to bites.

Cherry Blossoms

Cecil Cowdrey — Mary B. Black

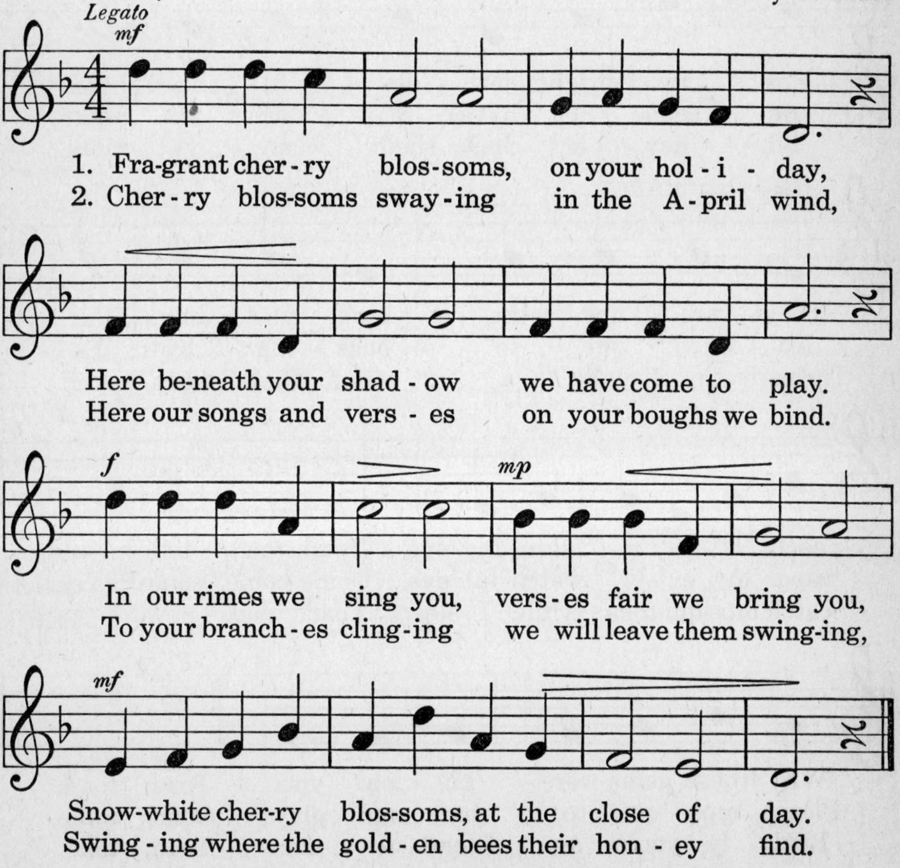
Legato
mf
1. Fra-grant cher-ry blos-soms, on your hol-i-day,
2. Cher-ry blos-soms sway-ing in the A-pril wind,
Here be-neath your shad-ow we have come to play.
Here our songs and vers-es on your boughs we bind.
f
mp
In our rimes we sing you, vers-es fair we bring you,
To your branch-es cling-ing we will leave them swing-ing,
mf
Snow-white cher-ry blos-soms, at the close of day.
Swing-ing where the gold-en bees their hon-ey find.

All the World

Ethel Crowninshield — Ruth McConn Spencer

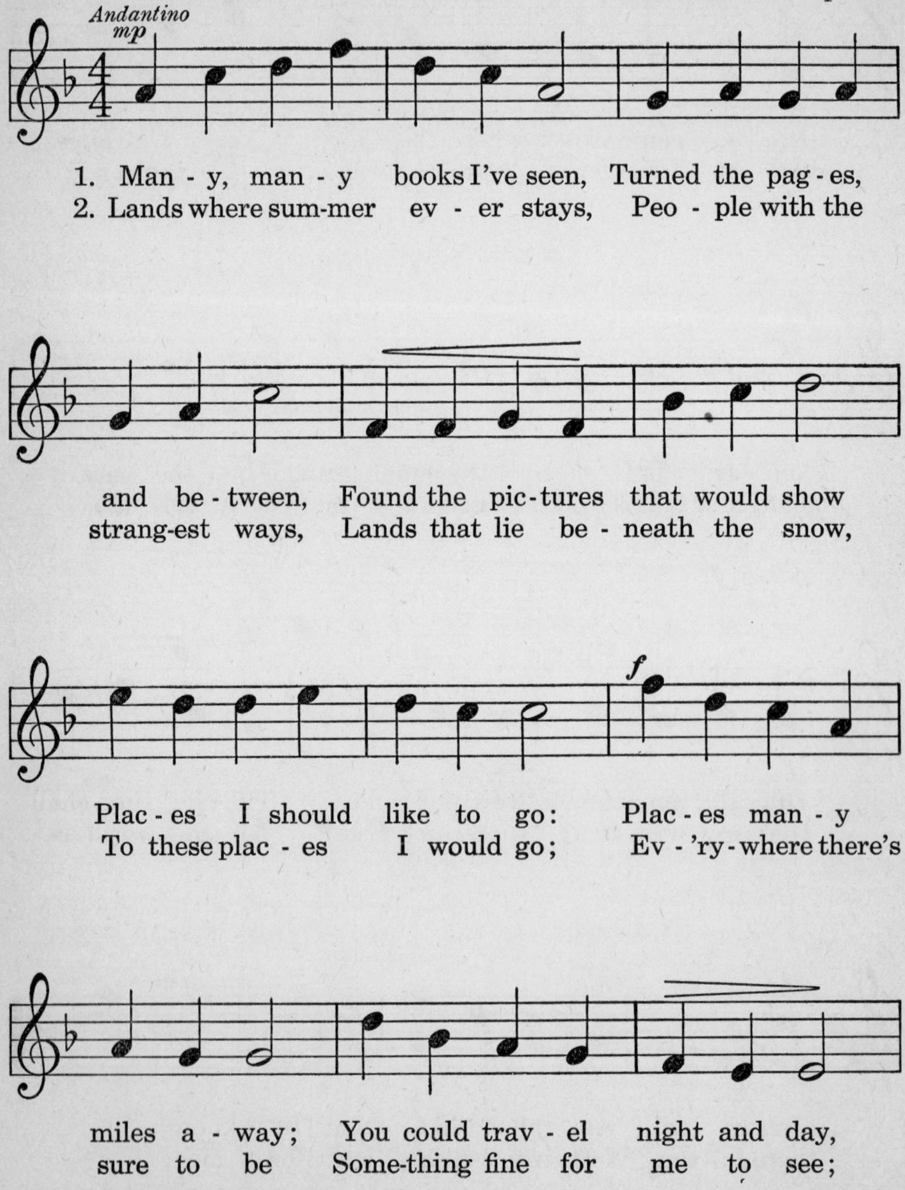
Andantino
mp
1. Man - y, man - y books I've seen, Turned the pag - es,
2. Lands where sum-mer ev - er stays, Peo - ple with the
and be - tween, Found the pic - tures that would show
strang-est ways, Lands that lie be - neath the snow,
f
Plac - es I should like to go: Plac - es man - y
To these plac - es I would go; Ev - 'ry - where there's
miles a - way; You could trav - el night and day,
sure to be Some-thing fine for me to see;

Ere you'd come to where they are; Ver - y strange!
While at ev - 'ry jour - ney's end I might find

ver - y far! By the moun-tains, by the sea,
some new friend! Can you tell me what to do,

Oh, I hope they'll wait for me, Till the time shall
That my wish may soon come true? All the world is

come to go! All the world I want to know!
there to see, Wait - ing, wait-ing just for me.

The Lace Maker

Mary C. Gleitz — French-Canadian Folk Tune

Tranquillamente
1. I know a mak-er of lace, do you?
2. That's what the wind is a-bout to-day,
Hap-py and live-ly is he, · ·
Thread-ing the sun through the leaves; · ·
mf
Weav-ing the sun-light and shad-ows blue
Let us go out to the yard and play
Un-der ev-'ry tree. · ·
On the lace he weaves. · ·

See What Grace

Translated — ROTE — Christoph Wilibald Gluck

Semplice
1. With what sweet-ness, light-ly as a feath-er,
2. With what fresh-ness wave the grace-ful grass-es.
Pret-ty maid-ens trip-ping to-geth-er,
Fields are full of light-heart-ed lass-es;

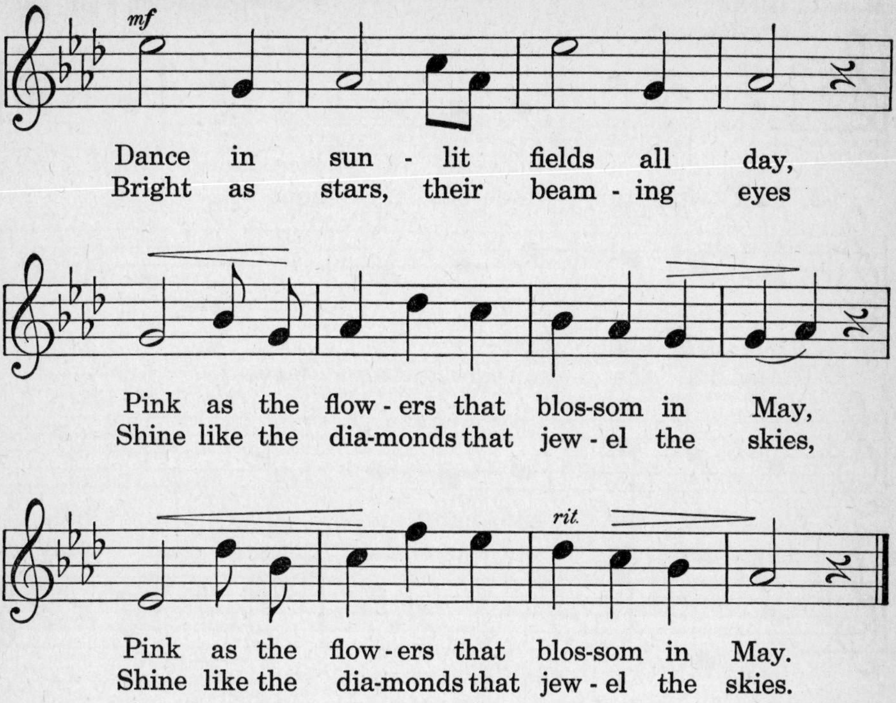
mf
Dance in sun - lit fields all day,
Bright as stars, their beam - ing eyes
Pink as the flow - ers that blos-som in May,
Shine like the dia-monds that jew - el the skies,
rit.
Pink as the flow - ers that blos-som in May.
Shine like the dia-monds that jew - el the skies.

Never a Sound

Rose Fyleman

Hungarian Folk Tune

Misterioso
mp
1. As I went a - walk - ing out one morn
2. Not a step I moved a - long the ground;
Where the har - vest fields were new - ly shorn,
Nev - er raised a hand nor made a sound;
Close be - fore me sat a lit - tle bun - ny,
But the bun - ny hopped a - long a fur - row
Ver - y cute and fun - ny,
To his lit - tle bur - row;
All a - mong the stalks of gold - en corn.
Nev - er e - ven stayed to look a - round.

Castle by the Sea

Clara Louise Kessler

Spanish Folk Tune

Con grazia
mf
1. Come to my cas - tle by the sea;
2. Come to my cas - tle, come a - way!
There the gold - en sun is shim - mer - ing.
O'er the sea the moon is glis - ten - ing.
Ol - ives and grapes on vine and tree
Hark to the mu - sic soft and gay!
Through their dusk - y leaves are glim - mer - ing,
All the si - lent night is lis - ten - ing.
Slow - ly rip - en - ing in the sun.
Sings the man - do - lin sweet and clear,
Oh, come with me! . .
"Oh, come a - way!" . .

Venetian Waters

Christine Turner Curtis

Italian Melody

Con espressione
mp
1. Gon - do - lier, pole on - ward and glide
2. Now the waves are pur - ple and deep,
O - ver the sun - ny blue rip - ple.
Un - der the gon - do - la sway - ing.
Light - ly, light - ly wash - es the tide, Spar - kles,
Sil - ver fish a - wak - en from sleep Shiv - er,
poco più moto
spar - kles, twin - kles be - side. Out to the sea,
shiv - er, laz - i - ly leap. Sea - foam is wet;
toss - ing and free, Far from the pal - ac - es
cast off your net; Gen - tly the breez - es are
f
sail - ing, Gon - do - lier, now steer to the
blow - ing. Gon - do - lier, come sing us a

west Through wa - ters gold - en and pal - ing.
song Of Ven - ice, gold - en and glow - ing.

The Art Extension Press, Inc.

Venetian Waters

Painted by the Italian artist Ettore Tito.
It is now in the Art Gallery in Budapest

Evening and Morning

Marjorie Knapp — Jean Jacques Rousseau

Larghetto
mp
1. Eve - ning comes : once more the sun has said good night.
2. Morn - ing comes : the gold - en sun shines down a - gain.
Shad-ows fall ; we watch for star-light gleams.
Skies are blue, the clouds are soft and bright.
Night brings rest all qui - et till the morn-ing light.
Birds a - wake ; we join them in a glad re-frain ;
mf
Eve - ning, gen - tle, gen - tle eve - ning,
Morn - ing, hap - py, hap - py morn - ing,
the time for sleep and dreams !
we greet you with de - light.

My Garden Sleeps

Clara Louise Kessler — French Folk Tune

Dolce cantabile
p
1. Swal-lows and the blue-birds have flown a - way,
2. Now my pret-ty gar - den has gone to sleep

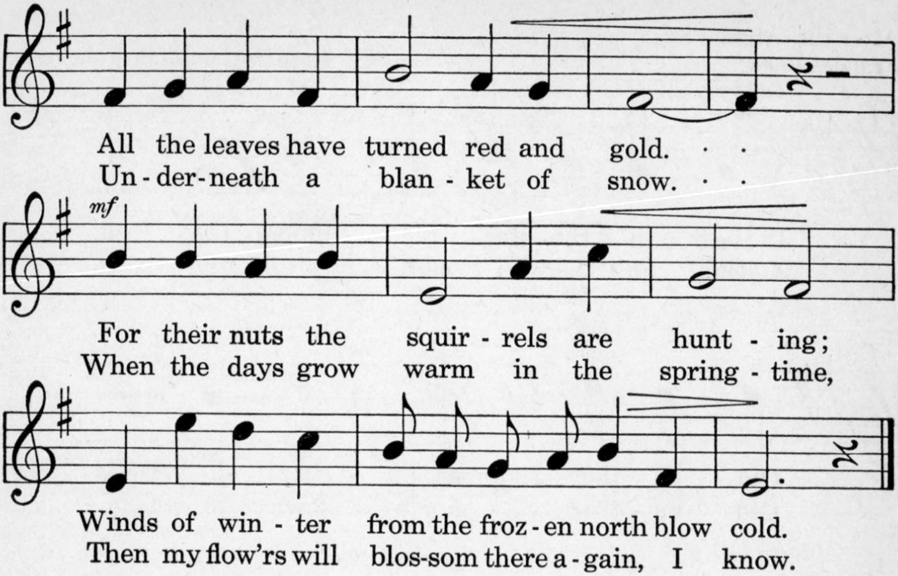
All the leaves have turned red and gold. . .
Un-der-neath a blan-ket of snow. . .
mf
For their nuts the squir-rels are hunt-ing;
When the days grow warm in the spring-time,
Winds of win-ter from the froz-en north blow cold.
Then my flow'rs will blos-som there a-gain, I know.

Clara Louise Kessler

In October

Yugoslavian Folk Tune

Animato

ROTE

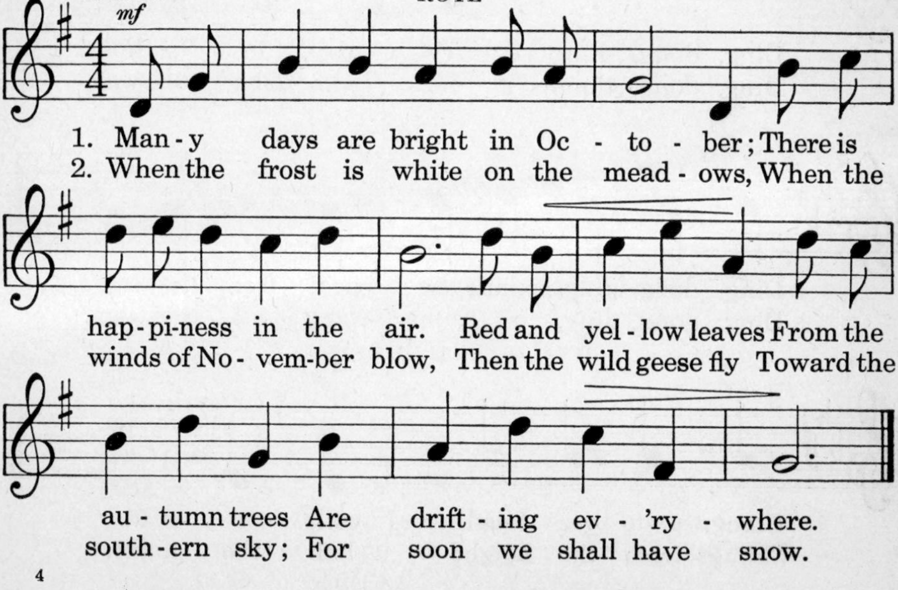
mf
1. Man-y days are bright in Oc-to-ber; There is
2. When the frost is white on the mead-ows, When the
hap-pi-ness in the air. Red and yel-low leaves From the
winds of No-vem-ber blow, Then the wild geese fly Toward the
au-tumn trees Are drift-ing ev-'ry-where.
south-ern sky; For soon we shall have snow.

The Bell Ringer

After the original by
Frances Ford

French-Canadian Folk Song

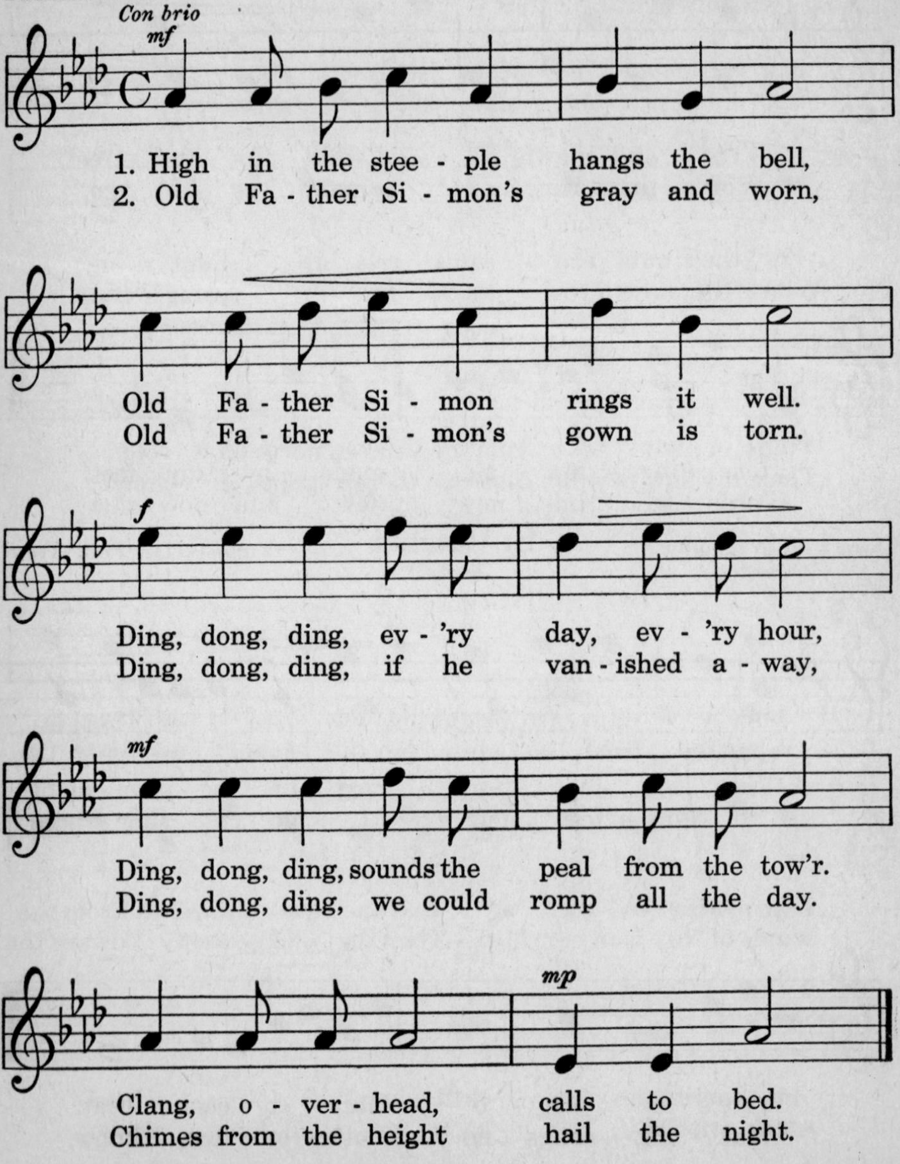
Con brio
mf
1. High in the stee - ple hangs the bell,
2. Old Fa - ther Si - mon's gray and worn,
Old Fa - ther Si - mon rings it well.
Old Fa - ther Si - mon's gown is torn.
f
Ding, dong, ding, ev - 'ry day, ev - 'ry hour,
Ding, dong, ding, if he van - ished a - way,
mf
Ding, dong, ding, sounds the peal from the tow'r.
Ding, dong, ding, we could romp all the day.
mp
Clang, o - ver - head, calls to bed.
Chimes from the height hail the night.

Making Songs

Louise Ayres Garnett | Mary B. Black

Legato
p
1. Up and down I walk on the street,
2. Words that rime I make as I go,
Hear - ing mu - sic made by my feet.
Words in time, now fast and now slow.
mf
When my foot - steps ring on the pave - ment
So my feet and I go a - sing - ing,
f
dim
There's an ech - o aft - er each beat.
Mak - ing songs no oth - er can know.

Spring Fever

Eleanor Farjeon

Irish Folk Tune

Con anima
mp
1. Ros - y Bet - sey, blue - eyed Mol - ly, Mol - ly,
2. Ros - y Bet - sey, blue - eyed Mol - ly, Mol - ly,
A - pril is the time for fol - ly, fol - ly.
Come and join the A - pril fol - ly, fol - ly.
Black - bird's shout rings round a - bout
Who can stay at home all day
And Jen - ny Wren is build - ing in the wil - low.
While Jen - ny Wren is build - ing in the wil - low?
f
Put off your coats of gray and brown!
Put on your prim - rose - col - ored gown!
Put off your clogs you wear in town!
Run in your green shoes out of town!

Run on the high - way up and down,
Run in the mead - ows up and down,

While the wren is build - ing in the wil - low.
Look - ing for the nest there in the wil - low.

The Brook

Ethel Crowninshield

Czech Folk Tune

Moderato
mf

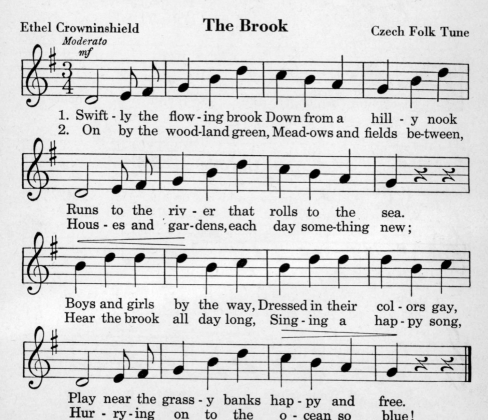

1. Swift - ly the flow - ing brook Down from a hill - y nook
2. On by the wood-land green, Mead-ows and fields be-tween,

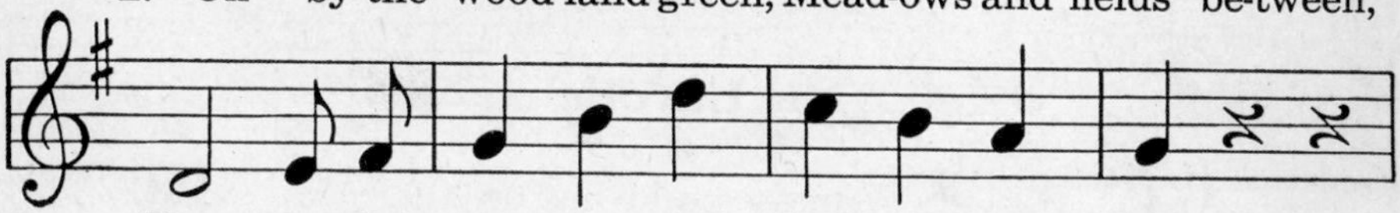

Runs to the riv - er that rolls to the sea.
Hous - es and gar-dens, each day some-thing new;

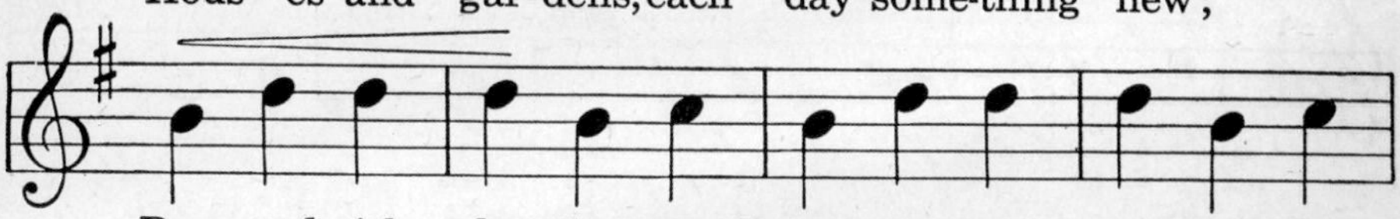

Boys and girls by the way, Dressed in their col - ors gay,
Hear the brook all day long, Sing - ing a hap - py song,

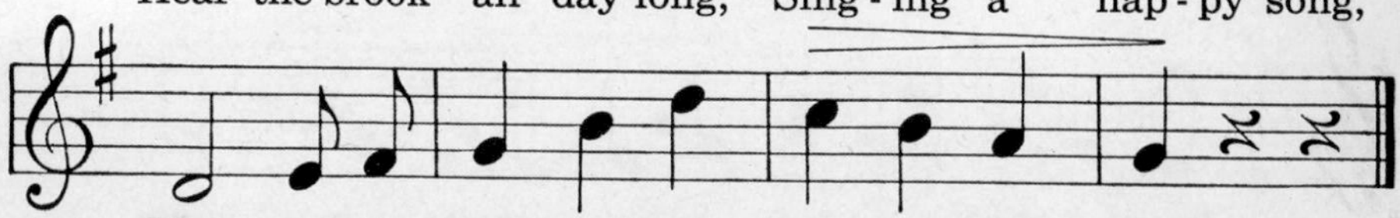

Play near the grass - y banks hap - py and free.
Hur - ry - ing on to the o - cean so blue!

The Gavotte

Frederick H. Martens — Jean Philippe Rameau

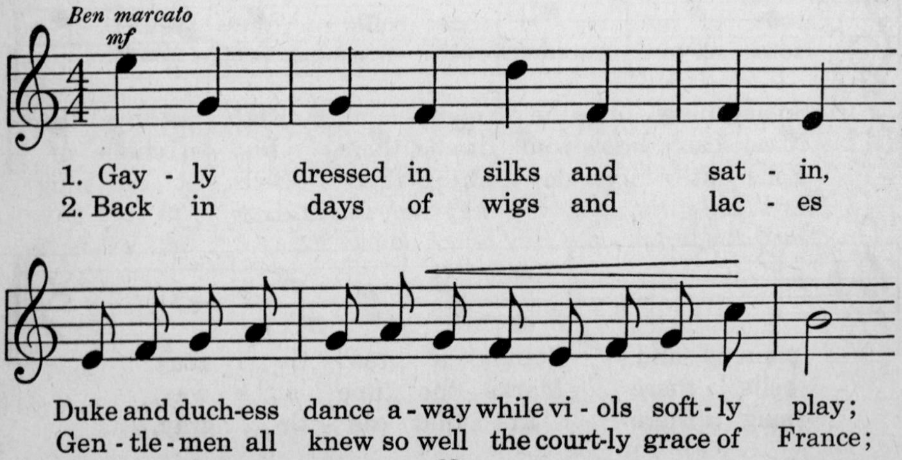
Ben marcato
mf
1. Gay - ly dressed in silks and sat - in,
2. Back in days of wigs and lac - es
Duke and duch-ess dance a - way while vi - ols soft - ly play;
Gen - tle - men all knew so well the court-ly grace of France;

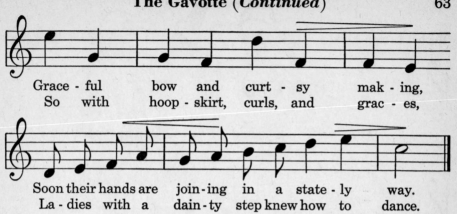

Grace - ful bow and curt - sy mak - ing,
So with hoop - skirt, curls, and grac - es,

Soon their hands are join - ing in a state - ly way.
La - dies with a dain - ty step knew how to dance.

The Lonely Castle

Nancy Byrd Turner — Spanish Folk Tune

Sostenuto
mp

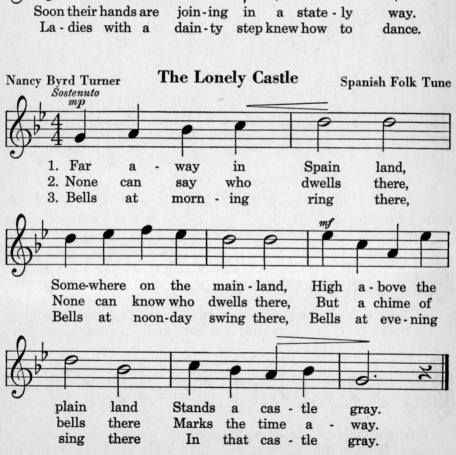

1. Far a - way in Spain land,
2. None can say who dwells there,
3. Bells at morn - ing ring there,

mf

Some-where on the main - land, High a - bove the
None can know who dwells there, But a chime of
Bells at noon-day swing there, Bells at eve - ning

plain land Stands a cas - tle gray.
bells there Marks the time a - way.
sing there In that cas - tle gray.

The Scissors-Grinder

ROTE

Rachel Lyman Field

Mary Root Kern

Giojoso
mf
O - ver the road when Spring be - gins
And pas - tures drop green to the bay,
Be - fore you have seen him a great way off
You can hear him call and say:
f
"Knives to grind!
Scis-sors to mend! Bring out your knives to - day!"

By Sweet Waters

After the original by
Christine Turner Curtis

Hassler-Bach

Largo
mp

By wa - ters sweet - ly wend - ing
His lit - tle lambs He's tend - ing,

Where grass is silk - y and fine,
The gen - tle Shep-herd di - vine.

On moun-tain or hill - top lead - ing

By steep and rug - ged rock;

mf

In sun - ny green pas - tures feed - ing,

rallentando

He guards His snow - y flock.

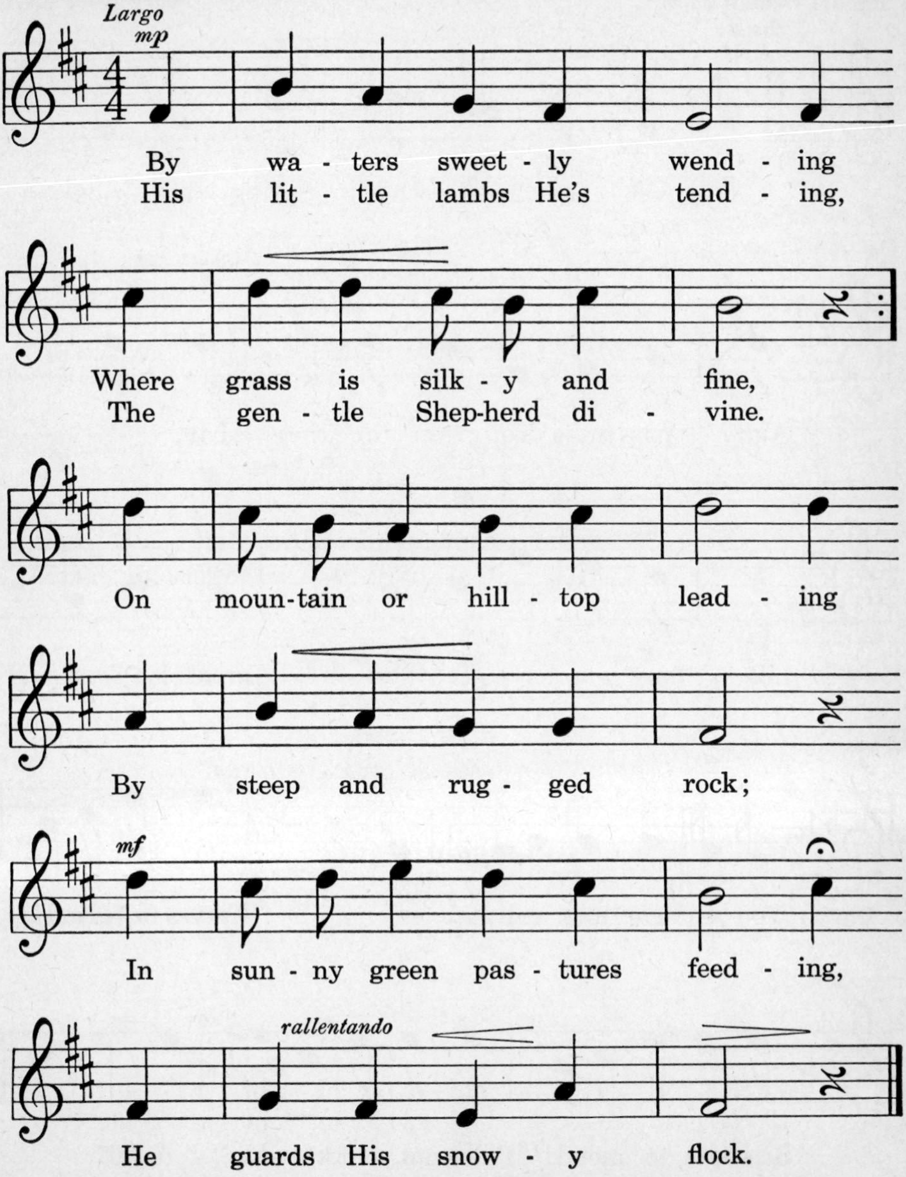

Left or Right

Louise Ayres Garnett

Polish Folk Tune

Con moto
mf
1. In one hand I'm hold-ing some-thing sweet; It is round and made with spic-es good to eat. If you choose the hand that holds it, left or right, You shall be the first to take a bite. . .
2. Should you choose the oth-er, this we'll do; I will have bite one and you may have bite two. So it's lit-tle mat-ter which you chance to name, We'll di-vide the cook-ie just the same. . .

Hungarian Dance

After the original by
Blanche Jennings Thompson

Hungarian Folk Song

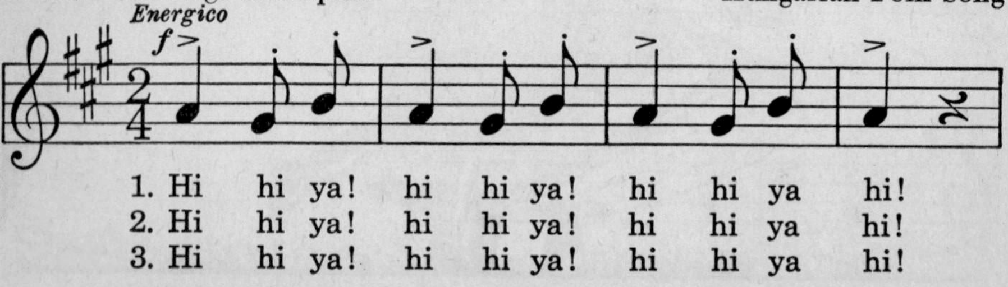
Energico
f
1. Hi hi ya! hi hi ya! hi hi ya hi!
2. Hi hi ya! hi hi ya! hi hi ya hi!
3. Hi hi ya! hi hi ya! hi hi ya hi!

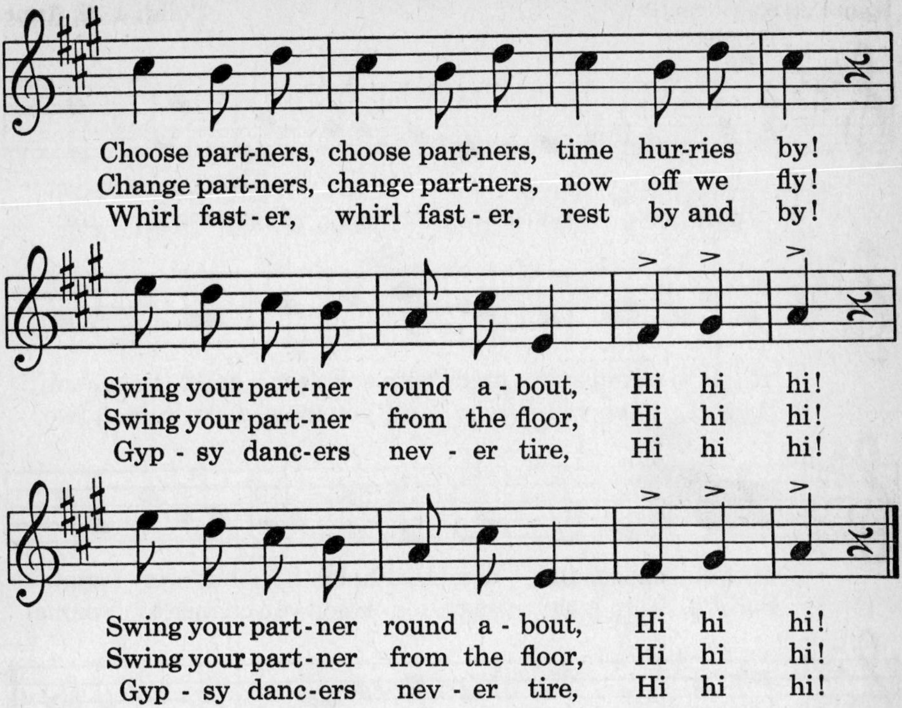
Choose part-ners, choose part-ners, time hur-ries by!
Change part-ners, change part-ners, now off we fly!
Whirl fast-er, whirl fast-er, rest by and by!
Swing your part-ner round a-bout, Hi hi hi!
Swing your part-ner from the floor, Hi hi hi!
Gyp-sy danc-ers nev-er tire, Hi hi hi!
Swing your part-ner round a-bout, Hi hi hi!
Swing your part-ner from the floor, Hi hi hi!
Gyp-sy danc-ers nev-er tire, Hi hi hi!

Bluebells and Fairies

Rose Fyleman

Mary B. Black

Leggiero
mp
1. Through the moon - lit wood - land sound - ing,
2. Fair - y sights and sounds will greet you,
Ting - a - ling - a - ling the blue - bells play;
Ring - a - ding - a - ding, oh, haste a - long;
Through the moss - y lanes re - sound - ing,
Fair - y part - ners wait to meet you.
Ting - a - ling - a - ling - ting - tay.
Ring - a - ding - a - ding, ding - dong!
mf
Leave your flow - er - y scent - ed beds,
Come, oh come to the moon - light ball,
Lis - ten to the bells, you sleep - y heads.
Has - ten to the danc - ing one and all.

f
mp
Ting-a - ling - a - ling and ting - a - ling - a - ling, Oh,
Ring-a - ding - a - ding and ring - a - ding - a - ding, Oh,

pp
ting - a - ling - a - ling - ting - tay.
ring - a - ding - a - ding, ding - dong.

English version by
Rose Fyleman

At the Fireplace

Hungarian Folk Song

Dolce espressivo

mp
p
1. Keen the wind and cold the night, Cold the night;
2. Dark and cheer-less barn and byre,[1] Barn and byre;

mf
Moon and stars are frost - y bright. Bit - ter times the
On - ly we be - side the fire Sit and read, with

p
win - ter brings To all furred and feath-ered things.
hap - py looks, Our en - chant - ing sto - ry books.

[1] Byre means a shed for cows.

The Broom and the Shovel

ROTE

Edward Lear — **Frederic Daly**

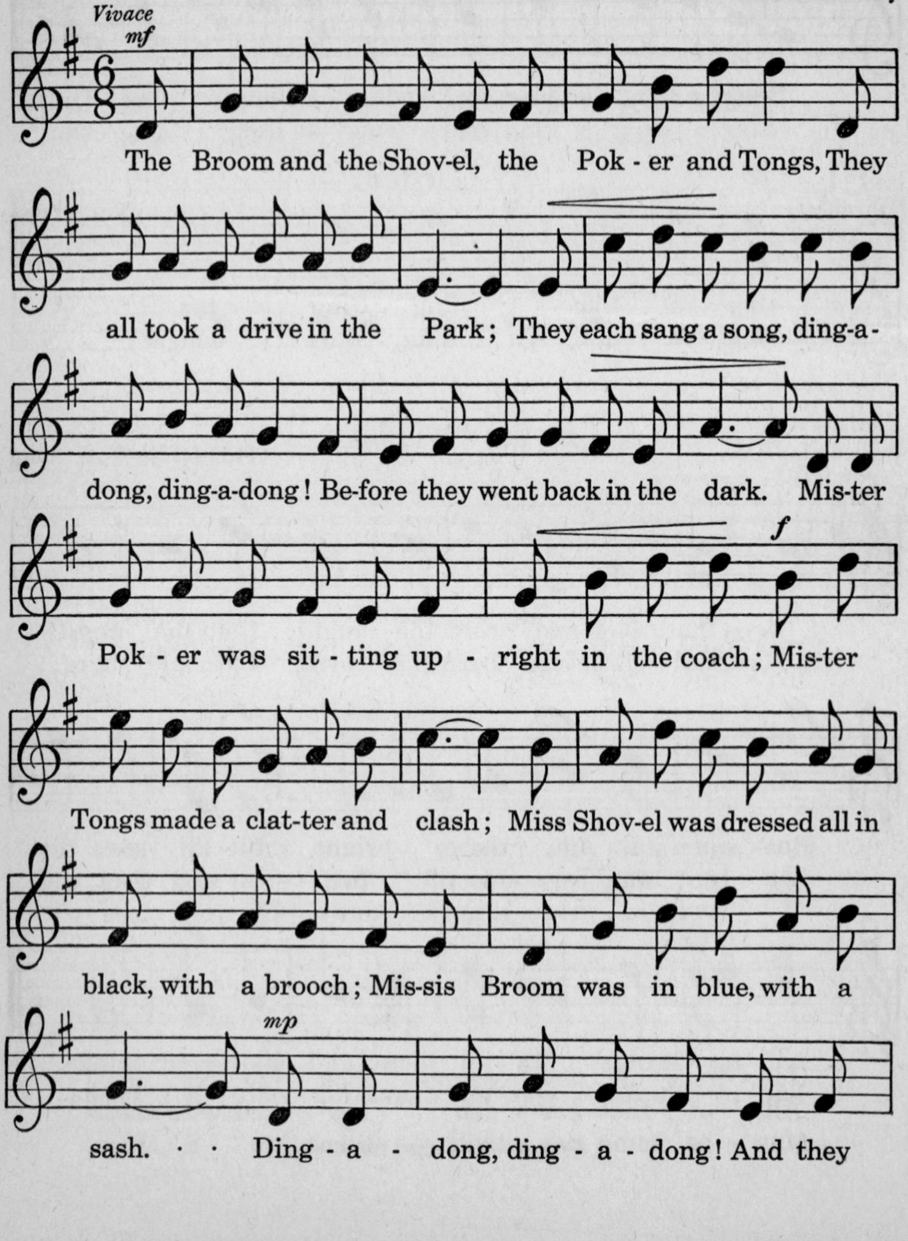
Vivace
mf
The Broom and the Shov-el, the Pok - er and Tongs, They
all took a drive in the Park; They each sang a song, ding-a-
dong, ding-a-dong! Be-fore they went back in the dark. Mis-ter
f
Pok - er was sit - ting up - right in the coach; Mis-ter
Tongs made a clat-ter and clash; Miss Shov-el was dressed all in
black, with a brooch; Mis-sis Broom was in blue, with a
mp
sash. · · Ding - a - dong, ding - a - dong! And they

all sang a song. Ding-a-dong! And they all sang a song.

My Garden

Marchette Gaylord Chute — German Folk Tune

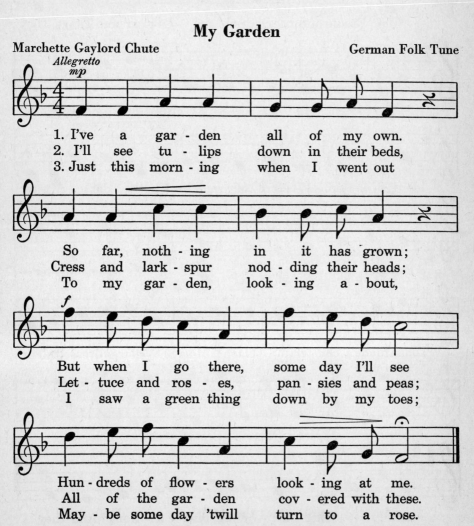

1. I've a gar - den all of my own.
2. I'll see tu - lips down in their beds,
3. Just this morn - ing when I went out

So far, noth - ing in it has grown;
Cress and lark - spur nod - ding their heads;
To my gar - den, look - ing a - bout,

But when I go there, some day I'll see
Let - tuce and ros - es, pan - sies and peas;
I saw a green thing down by my toes;

Hun - dreds of flow - ers look - ing at me.
All of the gar - den cov - ered with these.
May - be some day 'twill turn to a rose.

Freckles

Rachel Lyman Field | Mary Root Kern

Andantino
mp
Jane's hair is gold as a daf - fo - dil;
Blue as the sea are the eyes of Will;
Nan's lips are red - der than an - y rose,
But Dick has freck - les on his nose;
mf
Al - most as man - y, I should say,
ad libitum
As stars in the Milk - y Way.

Three Ponies

English version by
Eleanor Farjeon

Danish Folk Song

Marcato
mf
1. What will you ride on?
2. What will you ride on?
3. What will you ride on?
I'll ride a nut - brown po - ny;
I'll ride a coal - black po - ny;
I'll ride a snow - white po - ny;
Hemp - en hal - ter, i - ron bit,
Scar - let sad - dle, silk - en reins,
Sil - ver bri - dle, gold - en girth,
On his back a - stride I sit.
I will cross Sa - ha - ra's plains.
I will trav - el round the earth.
Hey, my nut - brown po - ny!
Hey, my coal - black po - ny!
Hey, my snow - white po - ny!

Market Day

Nancy Byrd Turner | Thuringian Folk Tune

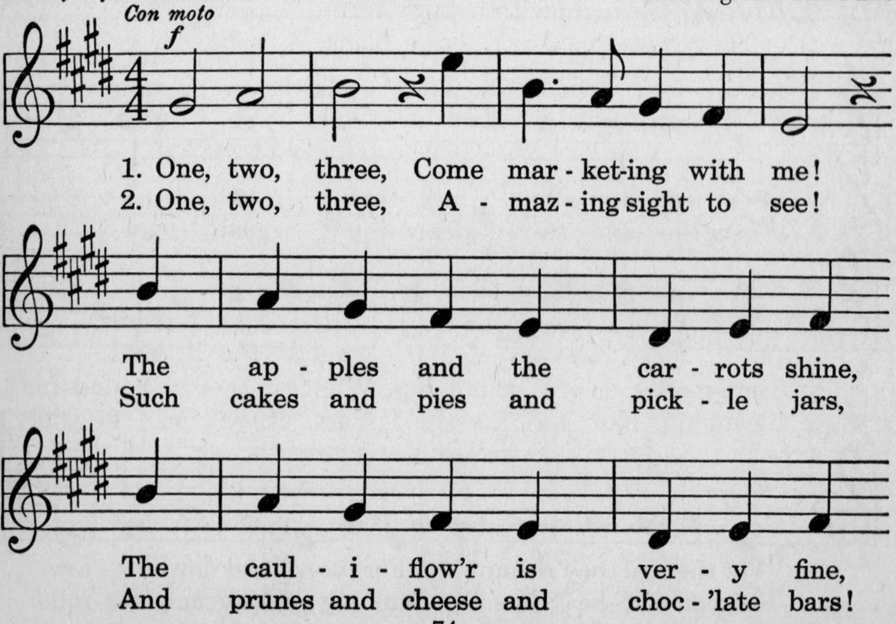
Con moto
f
1. One, two, three, Come mar - ket-ing with me!
2. One, two, three, A - maz - ing sight to see!
The ap - ples and the car - rots shine,
Such cakes and pies and pick - le jars,
The caul - i - flow'r is ver - y fine,
And prunes and cheese and choc - 'late bars!

And but - ter - beans and man - y greens,
Let's count our dimes a doz - en times:

And oth - er gar - den stuff.
We'll nev - er have e - nough.

Song of the Miners

Beatrice Wadhams

Polish Folk Tune

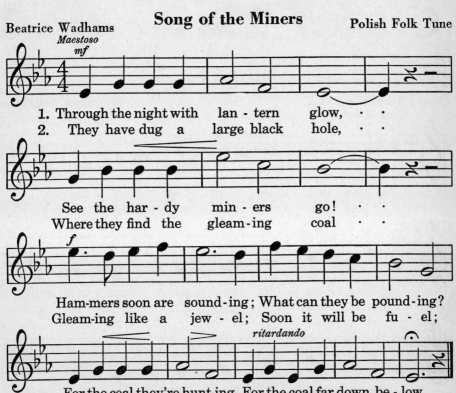

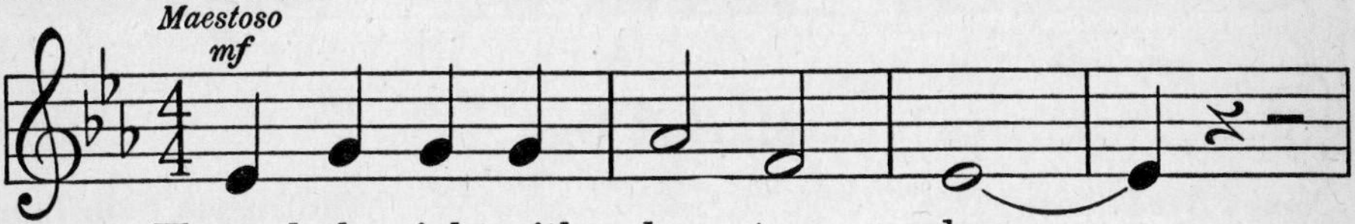
Maestoso
mf
1. Through the night with lan - tern glow, . .
2. They have dug a large black hole, . .

See the har - dy min - ers go! . .
Where they find the gleam - ing coal . .

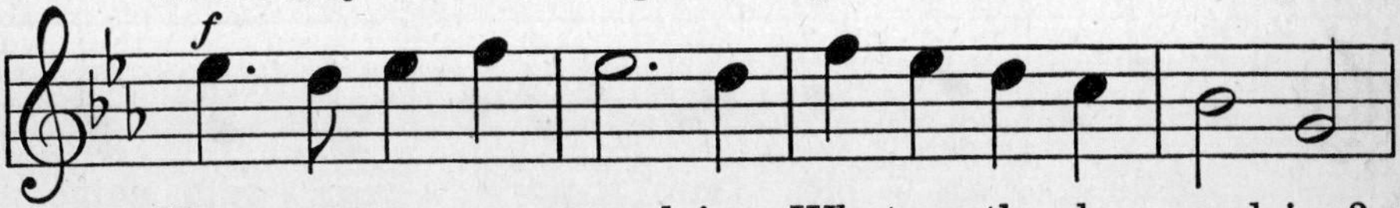
f
Ham-mers soon are sound - ing; What can they be pound - ing?
Gleam-ing like a jew - el; Soon it will be fu - el;

ritardando
For the coal they're hunt-ing, For the coal far down be - low.
Soon it will be fu - el, Mak-ing might-y en-gines roll.

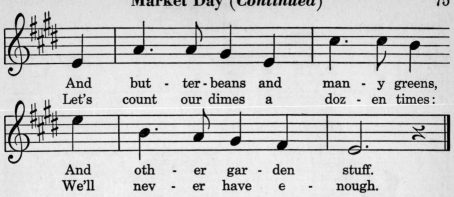

Thanksgiving Day

Marjorie Knapp ROTE Robert W. Gibb

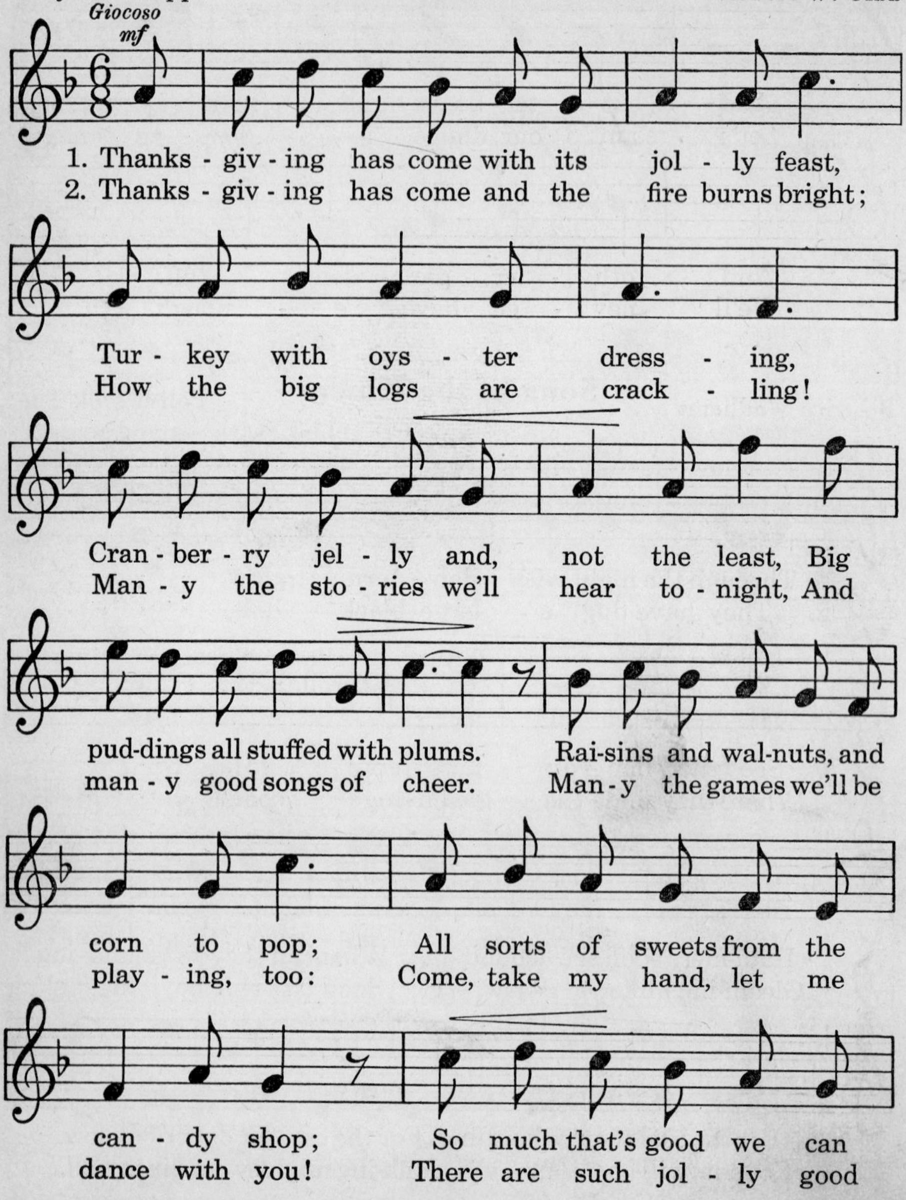
Giocoso
mf
1. Thanks - giv - ing has come with its jol - ly feast,
2. Thanks - giv - ing has come and the fire burns bright;
Tur - key with oys - ter dress - ing,
How the big logs are crack - ling!
Cran - ber - ry jel - ly and, not the least, Big
Man - y the sto - ries we'll hear to - night, And
pud-dings all stuffed with plums. Rai-sins and wal-nuts, and
man - y good songs of cheer. Man-y the games we'll be
corn to pop; All sorts of sweets from the
play - ing, too: Come, take my hand, let me
can - dy shop; So much that's good we can
dance with you! There are such jol - ly good

hard - ly stop. Once more Thanks-giv-ing Day comes.
things to do. Once more Thanks-giv-ing is here.

Snow Time

Lucy K. Milburn — Russian Folk Tune

Moderato
mp

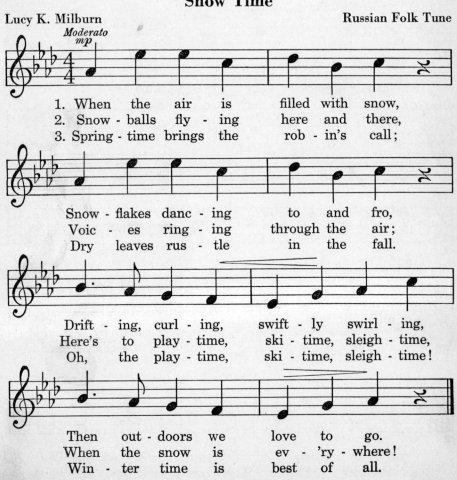

1. When the air is filled with snow,
2. Snow - balls fly - ing here and there,
3. Spring - time brings the rob - in's call;

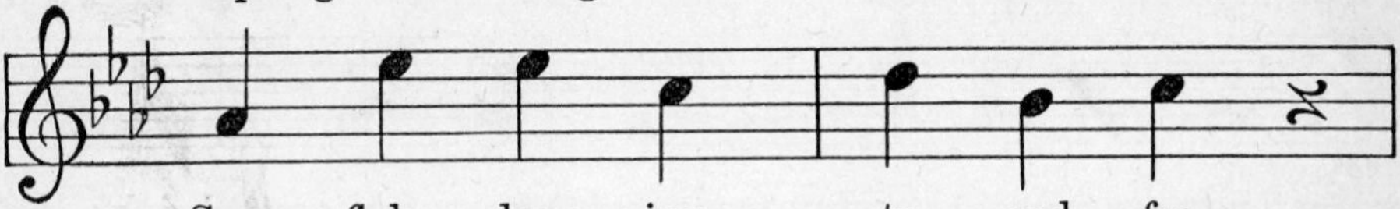

Snow - flakes danc - ing to and fro,
Voic - es ring - ing through the air;
Dry leaves rus - tle in the fall.

Drift - ing, curl - ing, swift - ly swirl - ing,
Here's to play - time, ski - time, sleigh - time,
Oh, the play - time, ski - time, sleigh - time!

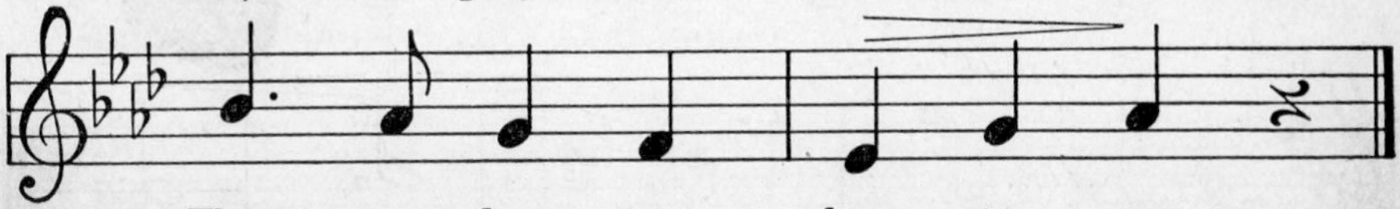

Then out - doors we love to go.
When the snow is ev - 'ry - where!
Win - ter time is best of all.

Little Ship

Hope Ann Rhodes

Norwegian Folk Tune

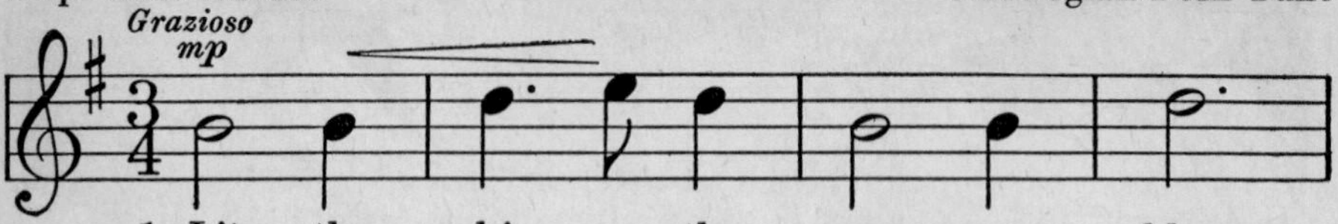

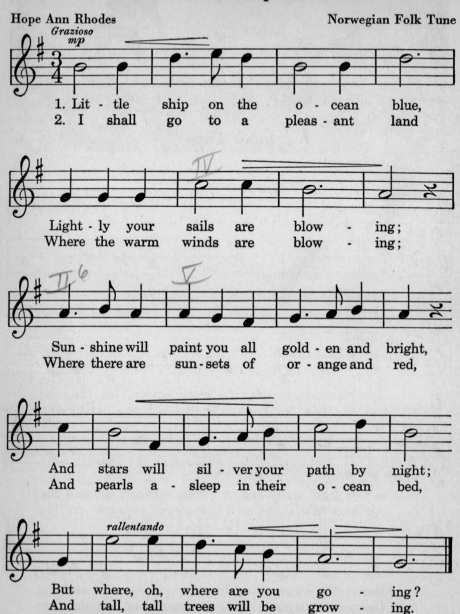

1. Lit - tle ship on the o - cean blue,
2. I shall go to a pleas - ant land

Light - ly your sails are blow - ing;
Where the warm winds are blow - ing;

Sun - shine will paint you all gold - en and bright,
Where there are sun - sets of or - ange and red,

And stars will sil - ver your path by night;
And pearls a - sleep in their o - cean bed,

But where, oh, where are you go - ing?
And tall, tall trees will be grow - ing.

Harvest Dance

Frederick H. Martens — Polish Folk Tune

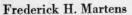

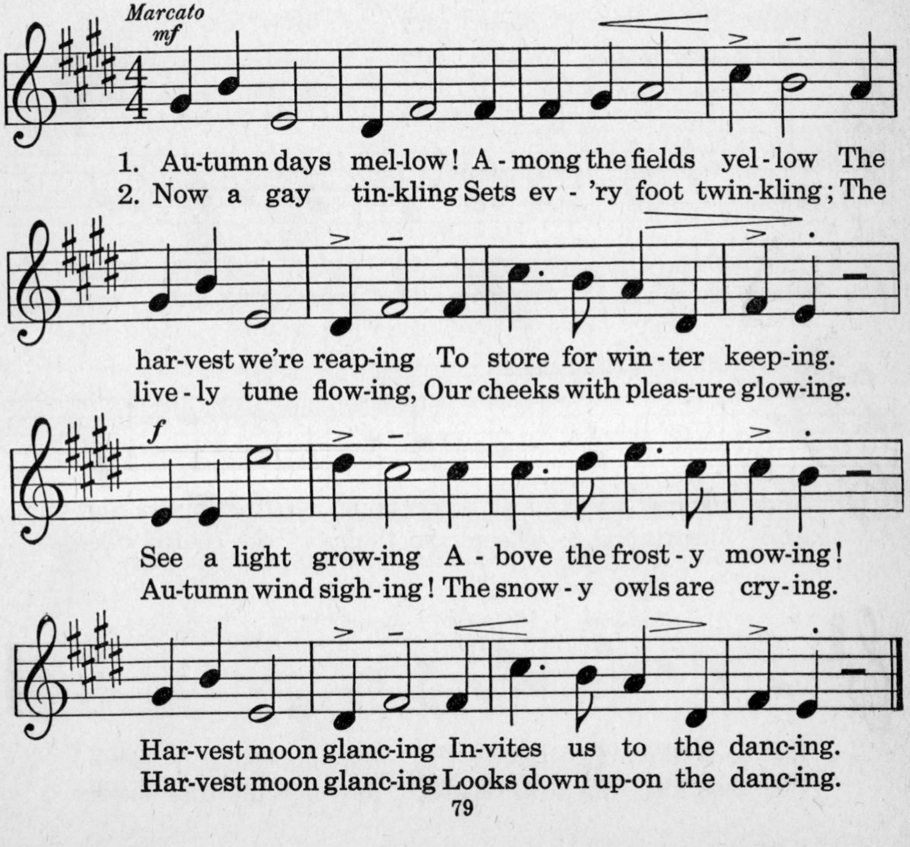
Marcato
mf
1. Au-tumn days mel-low! A - mong the fields yel - low The
2. Now a gay tin-kling Sets ev - 'ry foot twin-kling; The
har-vest we're reap-ing To store for win - ter keep-ing.
live - ly tune flow-ing, Our cheeks with pleas-ure glow-ing.
f
See a light grow-ing A - bove the frost - y mow-ing!
Au-tumn wind sigh-ing! The snow - y owls are cry - ing.
Har-vest moon glanc-ing In-vites us to the danc-ing.
Har-vest moon glanc-ing Looks down up-on the danc-ing.

Riding through the Snow

Louise Ayres Garnett

Russian Folk Tune

Con brio
f
1. Ride the road to some-where! Ho - la, hal - loo!
2. Bells are on the bri - dles. Ho - la, hal - loo!
Hors-es step proud-ly and we sit them proud-ly, too.
Ring, bells, your gay-est as we cut the miles in two!
Where shall we go, does an - y - bod - y know?
Shout to the sun and hur - ry, ev - 'ry - one;
We'll ride with sing-ing and with laugh - ter through the snow!
Day-light is go - ing and our ride is just be - gun.
Black are the hors - es and white is the scene;
Fields fly - ing past, with a riv - er be - tween;
ritardando
We look like fig-ures on a mov-ing-pic-ture screen.
We look like fig-ures on a mov-ing-pic-ture screen.

Hiking Song

Frederick H. Martens

German Folk Tune

Vivace
mf
1. Here we are!
2. Here we are!
U - pi-dee, u - pi - da! Let the shout-ing car - ry far!
U - pi-dee, u - pi - da! We have rea - son to hur - rah!
U - pi - dee, u - pi - da! Joy - ous - ly we sing!
U - pi - dee, u - pi - da! Joy - ous - ly we sing!
We are off with spir-its gay On a hik - ing hol - i - day.
As we gain the hill-top rise, All the world be - fore us lies.
f
U - pi - dee, u - pi - da! Hear our voic - es ring!
U - pi - dee, u - pi - da! Down the road we swing!

Christmas is Coming

English version by
Rose Fyleman

Polish Folk Song

1. Christ-mas is com - ing; oh, the hap - py time!
2. Far in the for - est stands a lit - tle tree,
3. Christ-mas is com - ing; glad we are and gay.

Christ - mas is com - ing; sing a mer - ry rime.
Wait - ing and long - ing for the days to be,
Christ - mas is com - ing; sing a roun-de - lay.

Tell me, what is Christ-mas bring-ing? Love and joy, and
When it shall be bright and shin-ing, Gar-lands in its
Soon in spite of win - try weath-er, All the world shall

gay bells ring - ing With a gold - en chime.
branch - es twin - ing, All for you and me.
make to - geth - er Lov - ing hol - i - day.

Song before Christmas

English version by
Cecil Cowdrey

German Folk Song

Leggiero
mp
1. Sing to - day a song of right good cheer.
2. Now's the time for keep-ing hol - i - day;
Sing, for Christ-mas Day will soon be here!
School doors close, and books are put a - way.
La la la la, mer - ry let us be.
La la la la, Christ-mas Day is near;
Soon we'll sing a - round the Christ - mas tree;
Good Saint Nich - o - las will soon be here;
Soon we'll sing a - round the Christ - mas tree.
Good Saint Nich - o - las will soon be here.

Christmas Eve

Ethel Crowninshield — Bohemian-Czech Folk Tune

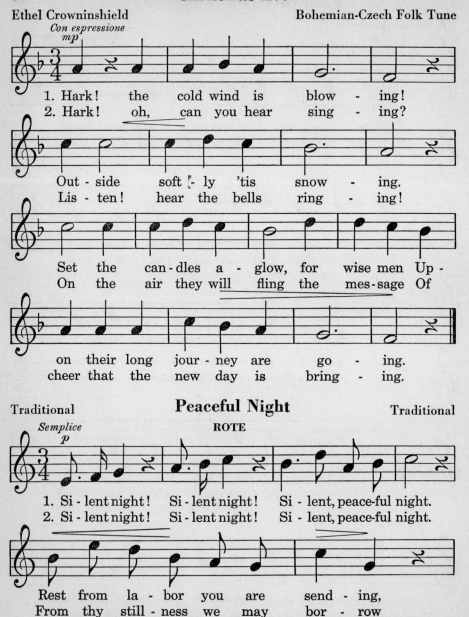

1. Hark! the cold wind is blow - ing!
2. Hark! oh, can you hear sing - ing?

Out - side soft - ly 'tis snow - ing.
Lis - ten! hear the bells ring - ing!

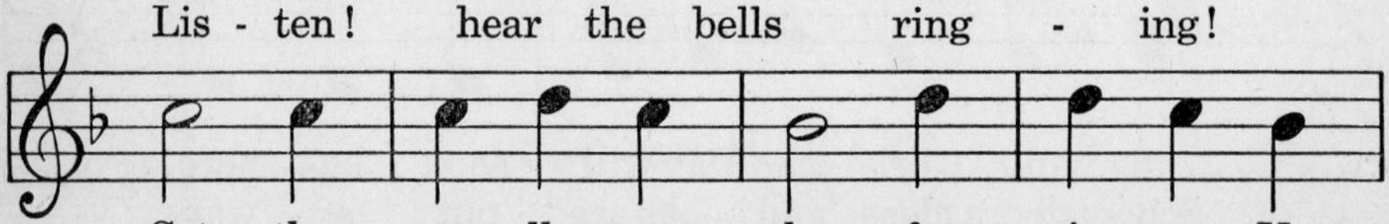

Set the can - dles a - glow, for wise men Up -
On the air they will fling the mes - sage Of

on their long jour - ney are go - ing.
cheer that the new day is bring - ing.

Peaceful Night

Traditional — Traditional

ROTE

1. Si - lent night! Si - lent night! Si - lent, peace-ful night.
2. Si - lent night! Si - lent night! Si - lent, peace-ful night.

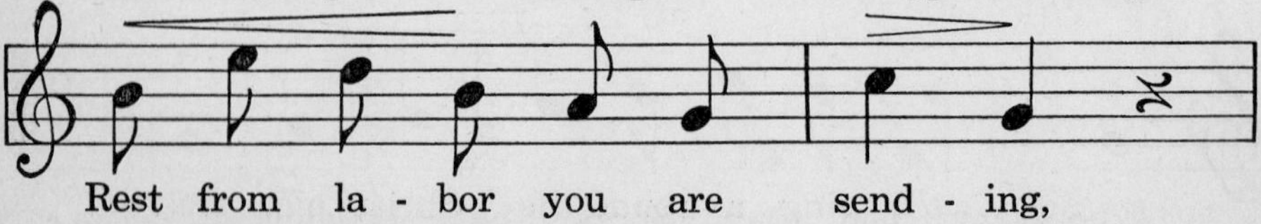

Rest from la - bor you are send - ing,
From thy still - ness we may bor - row

O'er a wea - ried world are bend - ing,
Peace and com - fort for the mor - row,
ritardando
Till the morn-ing light Ends the peace - ful, peace-ful night.
Sure that God's clear light Ends the si - lent, si - lent night.

A Christmas Song

Clara Louise Kessler

German Folk Tune

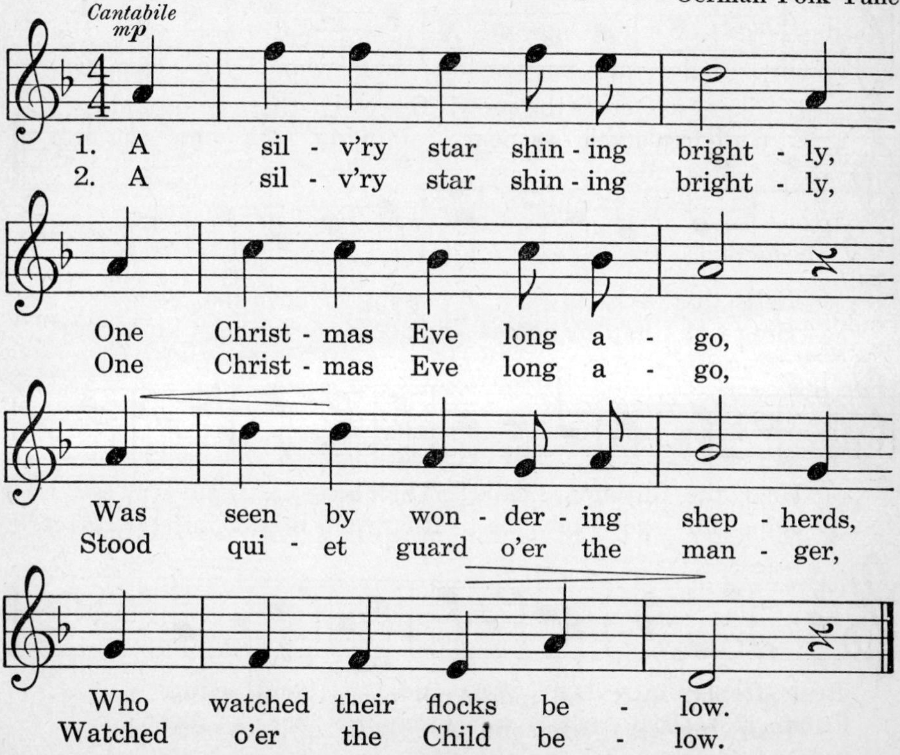
Cantabile
mp
1. A sil - v'ry star shin - ing bright - ly,
2. A sil - v'ry star shin - ing bright - ly,
One Christ - mas Eve long a - go,
One Christ - mas Eve long a - go,
Was seen by won - der - ing shep - herds,
Stood qui - et guard o'er the man - ger,
Who watched their flocks be - low.
Watched o'er the Child be - low.

Christmas

M. Louise Baum | Wolfgang Amadeus Mozart

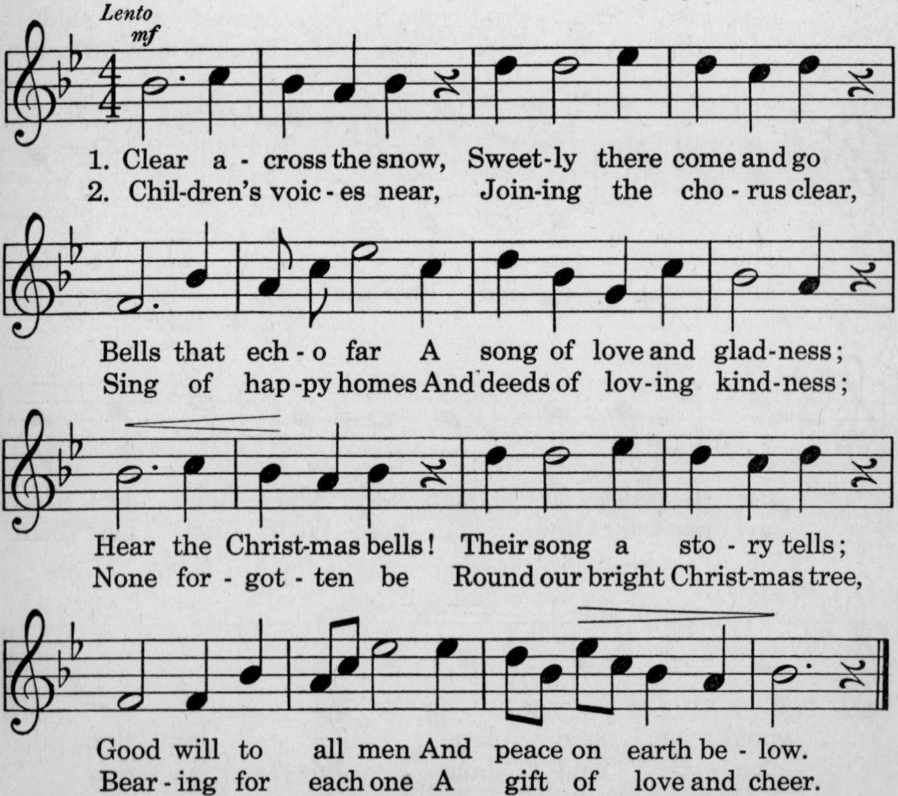
Lento
mf
1. Clear a - cross the snow, Sweet-ly there come and go
2. Chil-dren's voic - es near, Join-ing the cho - rus clear,
Bells that ech - o far A song of love and glad-ness;
Sing of hap-py homes And deeds of lov-ing kind-ness;
Hear the Christ-mas bells! Their song a sto - ry tells;
None for - got - ten be Round our bright Christ-mas tree,
Good will to all men And peace on earth be - low.
Bear - ing for each one A gift of love and cheer.

Jane Jess Jollander

Rose Fyleman

Hungarian Folk Tune

Giocoso
mf
1. Jane Jess Jol - lan - der, She had an an - cient
2. Jane Jess Jol - lan - der, She al - ways spoke with
gan - der. "And what could be grand - er?" said
can - dor, And folk rath - er banned her. Poor
Jane Jol - lan - der. "To say he's fool - ish Is
Jane Jol - lan - der! "But that's no mat - ter; I
just a wick - ed slan - der, And slan - der is
have my dar - ling gan - der; We'll just let them
ghoul - ish," said Jane Jol - lan - der.
chat - ter," said Jane Jol - lan - der.

Whirligig

Louise Ayres Garnett — Friedrich Frischenschlager[1]

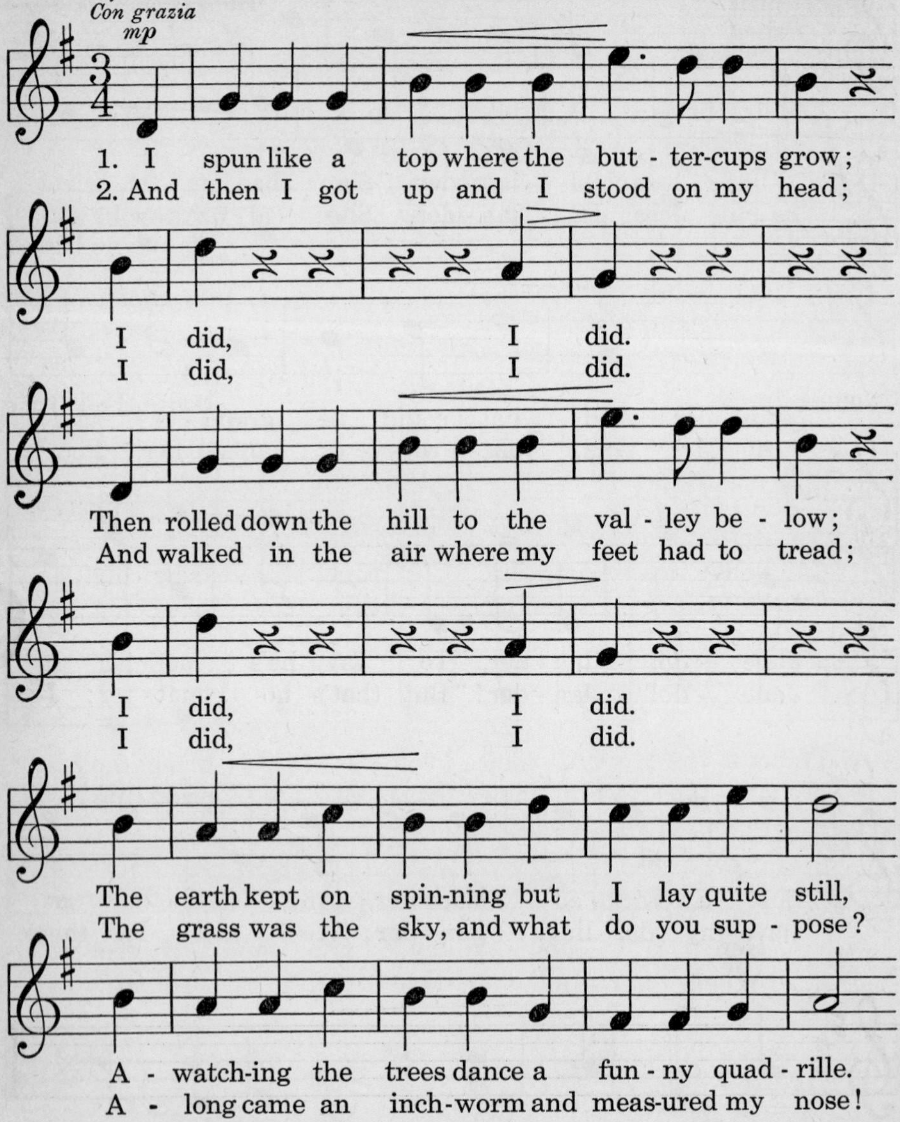
Con grazia
mp
1. I spun like a top where the but - ter-cups grow;
2. And then I got up and I stood on my head;
I did, I did.
I did, I did.
Then rolled down the hill to the val - ley be - low;
And walked in the air where my feet had to tread;
I did, I did.
I did, I did.
The earth kept on spin-ning but I lay quite still,
The grass was the sky, and what do you sup - pose?
A - watch-ing the trees dance a fun - ny quad - rille.
A - long came an inch-worm and meas-ured my nose!

[1] Used by permission of the original publishers, Universal Edition, Vienna; contained in "12 Kinderlieder" by Frischenschlager.

f
And then I rolled up - hill;
I shooed it with my toes;
p
I did, I did.
I did, I did.

Sigmund Spaeth

Holiday

Danish Folk Tune

Allegro
mf
1. Bells are ring - ing, time for sing - ing.
2. Bells are ring - ing, time for sing - ing.
What's the word their voic - es are bring - ing?
What's the word their voic - es are bring - ing?
Here's a hol - i - day, fine and cheer - y;
What a jol - ly day, nev - er drear - y;
f
Sun - shine calls out - side the door.
Let's not waste a mo - ment more.

The Cake

English version by
Laura E. Richards

Polish Folk Song

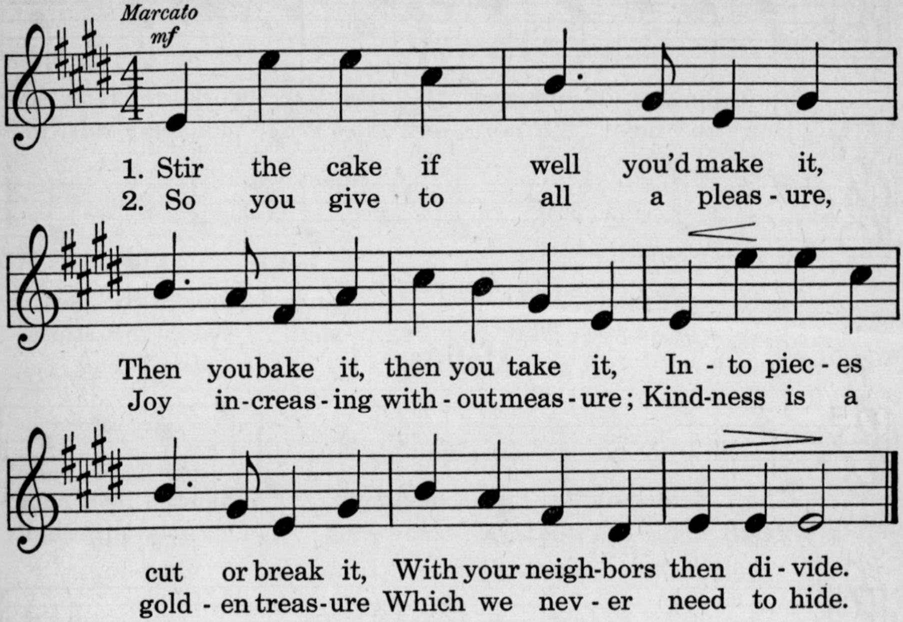
Marcato
mf
1. Stir the cake if well you'd make it,
2. So you give to all a pleas - ure,
Then you bake it, then you take it, In - to piec - es
Joy in-creas - ing with - out meas - ure; Kind-ness is a
cut or break it, With your neigh-bors then di - vide.
gold - en treas-ure Which we nev - er need to hide.

Fisherman's Song

Blanche Jennings Thompson

Finnish Folk Tune

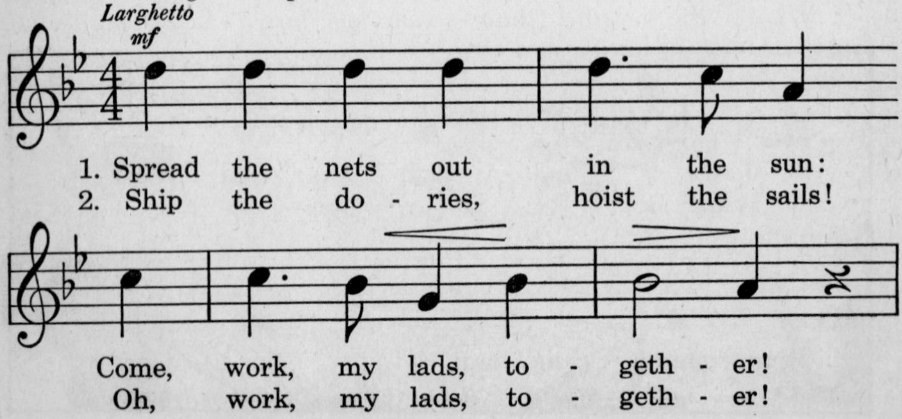
Larghetto
mf
1. Spread the nets out in the sun:
2. Ship the do - ries, hoist the sails!
Come, work, my lads, to - geth - er!
Oh, work, my lads, to - geth - er!

Mend the strands now, one by one. Oh, work, my lads, to -
Out to meet the north - ern gales We'll sail, my lads, to -
geth - er! When the fleet puts out to sea,
geth - er. Our good ship shall ride the storm,
The nets must all be mend - ed. When the fleet puts
Though loud the winds be blow - ing. Our good ship shall
meno mosso
out to sea, The nets must all be mend - ed.
ride the storm, Though loud the winds be blow - ing.

Firemen

ROTE

Ethel Crowninshield — Ethel Crowninshield

Energico
Too! too! The fire - men are com - ing!
Ev-'ry-one else will be still. En-gines and hose and the
big hook and lad - der Go by, rush - ing on up the
hill. Too! too! The fire is all o - ver;
Back to the sta-tion they go. I al-ways stand on the
edge of the curb; For one of the fire-men I know.

Hi Yi

After the original by
Marjorie Knapp

Hungarian Folk Song

Con spirito
mf
1. Clap your hands while we are shout - ing.
2. Clap your hands while we are danc - ing.
mp
Hi ya hi, hi yi! Then
Hi ya hi, hi yi! At
step out bold - ly, nev - er doubt - ing.
first re - treat - ing, then ad - vanc - ing.
f
Hi ya hi, hi yi! Oh,
Hi ya hi, hi yi! Now
sing a - way, hi yi! With voic - es gay, hi yi! Now
close we stand, hi yi! Come, take my hand, hi yi! How
one, two, three, hi yi! Come dance with me, hi yi hi!
smooth the floor, hi yi! Let's dance once more, hi yi hi!

Vesper Bells

English version by
Christine Turner Curtis

German Folk Song

Con grazia
mp
1. Bells from the tow'r car - ol the hour.
2. Glow - ing with light, an - gels in white,
3. Cra - dled and warm, here on my arm,
Come, lit - tle gold - en head, pi-geons are all a - bed;
Wing - ing a - bove the sun, give to my gold - en one
Dream of the wool - ly flocks feed-ing in mead - ow walks!
rall.
a tempo
Pur - ple and ros - y red, skies are in flow'r.
Eyes like the sum - mer sun, ten - der and bright.
Sleep, lit - tle Gold - i - locks, shel - tered from harm!

The Wind

Caroline A. Mason

Sigmund Spaeth

Legato
mp
1. Which - ev - er way the wind may blow,
2. My lit - tle bark sails not a - lone;
Some heart is glad to have it so;
A thou - sand fleets from ev - 'ry zone

Then blow it east or blow it west,
Are out up - on a thou - sand seas,
ad libitum
The wind that blows, · that wind is best.
And each a - waits · a fav - 'ring breeze.

Morning Hymn

Anonymous

Robert W. Gibb

Larghetto
mp
1. For flow'rs that bloom a - bout our feet,
2. For this new morn - ing with its light,
mf
For ten - der grass so fresh and sweet; For song of
For rest and shel - ter through the night; For health and
bird · and hum of bee; For all things fair · we
food, · for love and friends; For ev - 'ry - thing · Thy
mp
hear or see, Fa-ther in Heav'n, we thank Thee.
good-ness sends, Fa-ther in Heav'n, we thank Thee.

Music

Clara Louise Kessler

Danish Folk Tune

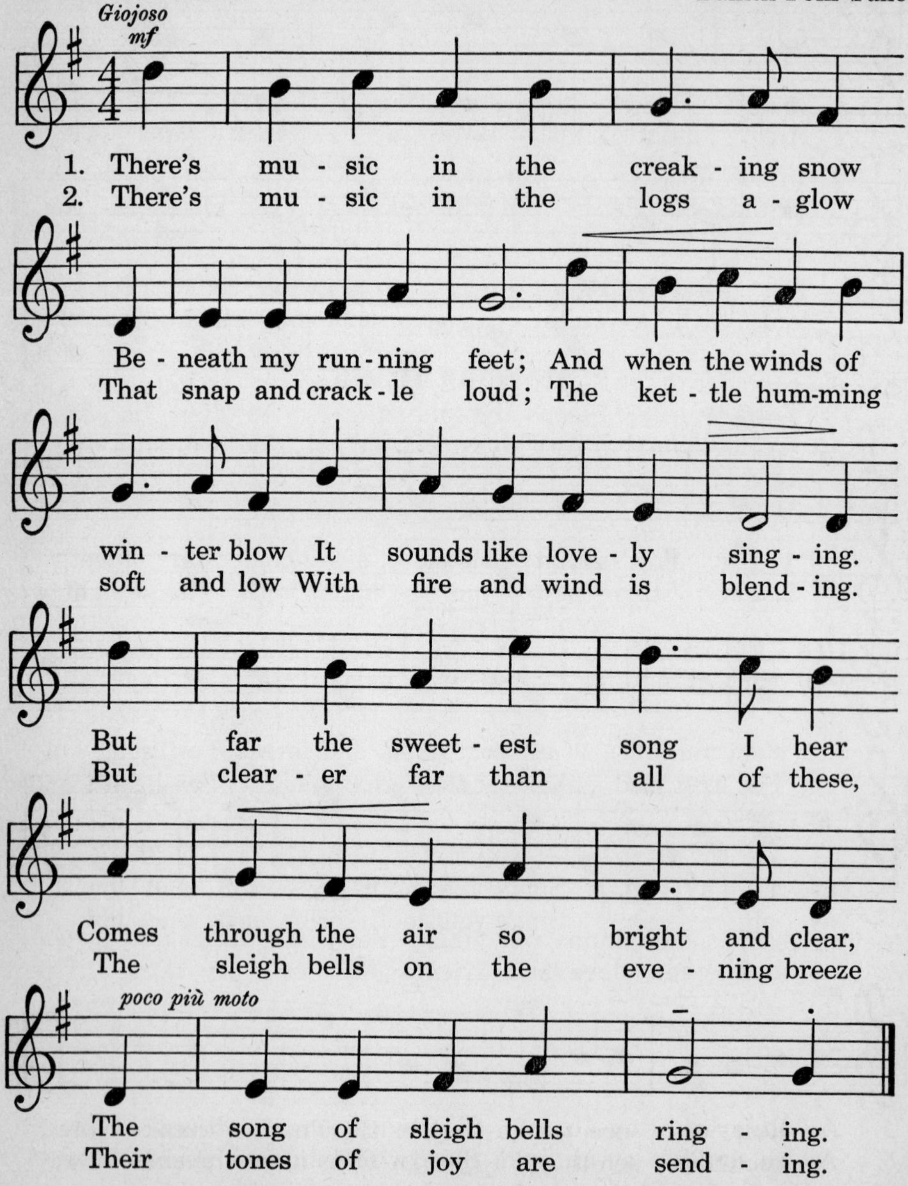
Giojoso
mf
1. There's mu - sic in the creak - ing snow
2. There's mu - sic in the logs a - glow
Be - neath my run - ning feet; And when the winds of
That snap and crack - le loud; The ket - tle hum-ming
win - ter blow It sounds like love - ly sing - ing.
soft and low With fire and wind is blend - ing.
But far the sweet - est song I hear
But clear - er far than all of these,
Comes through the air so bright and clear,
The sleigh bells on the eve - ning breeze
poco più moto
The song of sleigh bells ring - ing.
Their tones of joy are send - ing.

Indian Lullaby

Moiselle Renstrom — ROTE — Moiselle Renstrom

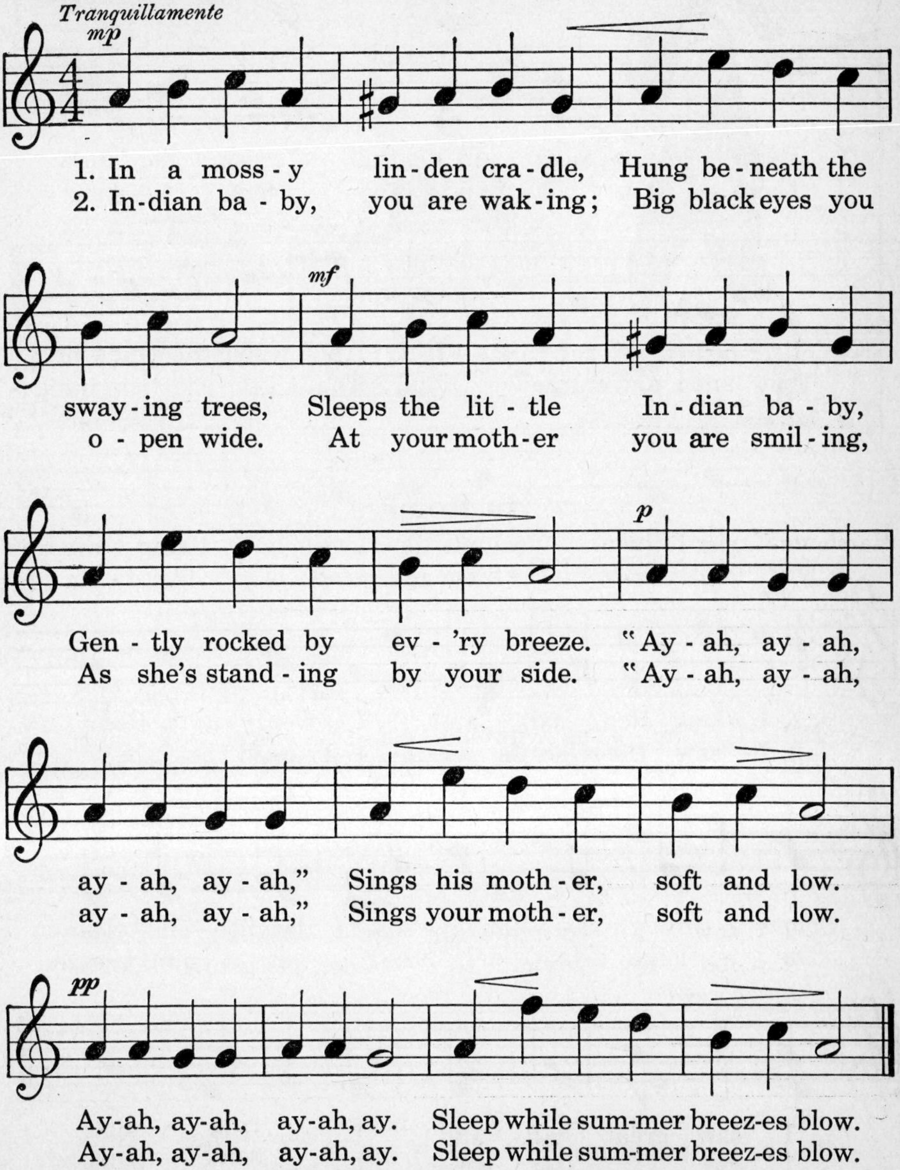
Tranquillamente
1. In a moss-y lin-den cra-dle, Hung be-neath the sway-ing trees, Sleeps the lit-tle In-dian ba-by, Gen-tly rocked by ev-'ry breeze. "Ay-ah, ay-ah, ay-ah, ay-ah," Sings his moth-er, soft and low. Ay-ah, ay-ah, ay-ah, ay. Sleep while sum-mer breez-es blow.
2. In-dian ba-by, you are wak-ing; Big black eyes you o-pen wide. At your moth-er you are smil-ing, As she's stand-ing by your side. "Ay-ah, ay-ah, ay-ah, ay-ah," Sings your moth-er, soft and low. Ay-ah, ay-ah, ay-ah, ay. Sleep while sum-mer breez-es blow.

In Rome

Marchette Gaylord Chute

Italian Folk Tune

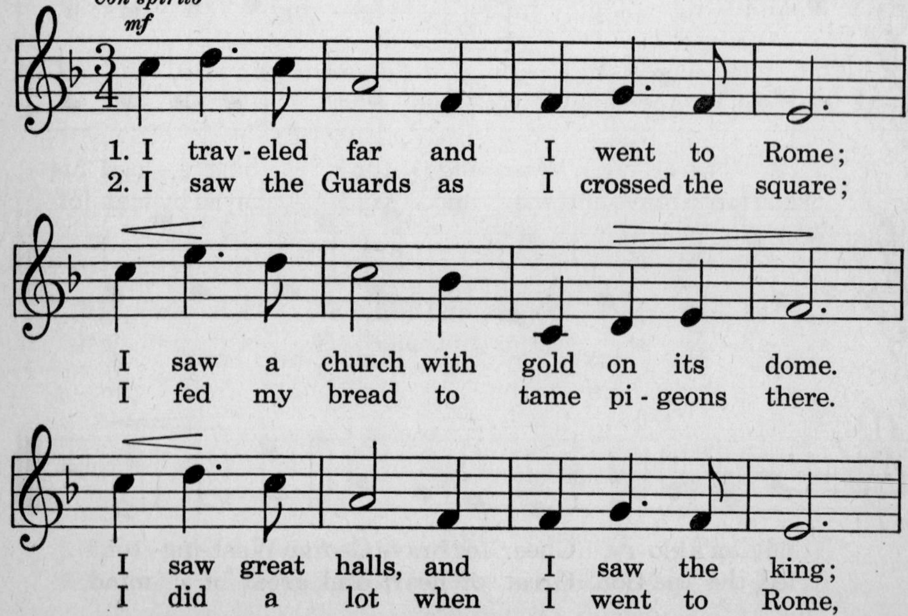
Con spirito
mf
1. I trav-eled far and I went to Rome;
2. I saw the Guards as I crossed the square;
I saw a church with gold on its dome.
I fed my bread to tame pi-geons there.
I saw great halls, and I saw the king;
I did a lot when I went to Rome,

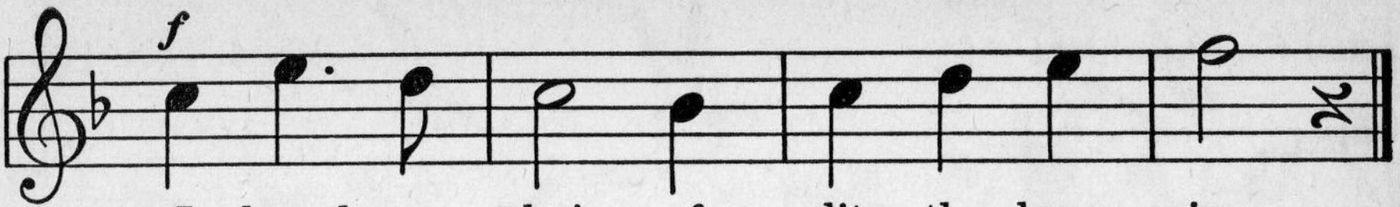

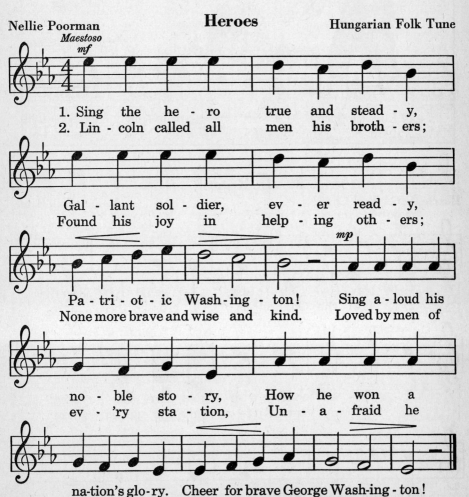

I heard a choir of lit - tle boys sing.
Now I am glad to be here at home.

Heroes

Nellie Poorman | Hungarian Folk Tune

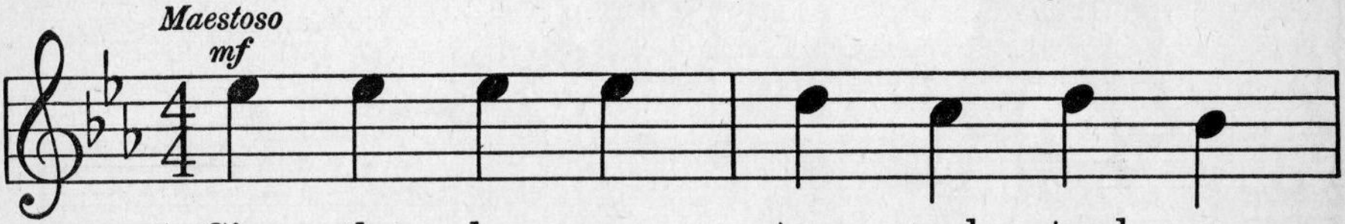

1. Sing the he - ro true and stead - y,
2. Lin - coln called all men his broth - ers;

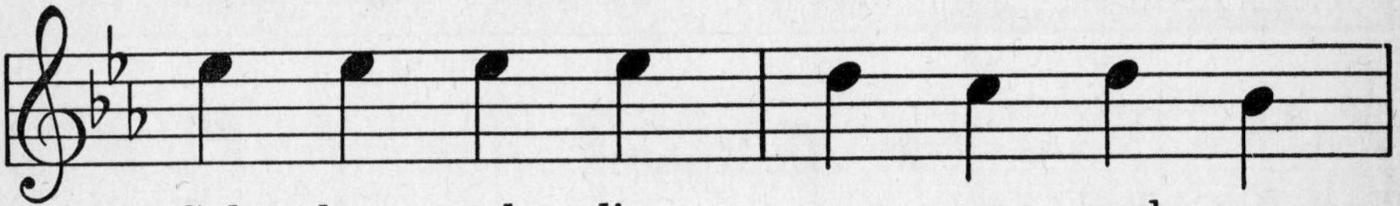

Gal - lant sol - dier, ev - er read - y,
Found his joy in help - ing oth - ers;

Pa - tri - ot - ic Wash - ing - ton! Sing a - loud his
None more brave and wise and kind. Loved by men of

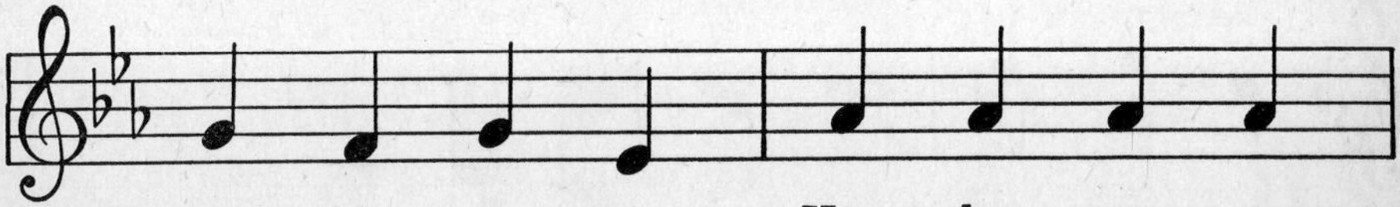

no - ble sto - ry, How he won a
ev - 'ry sta - tion, Un - a - fraid he

na-tion's glo-ry. Cheer for brave George Wash-ing - ton!
led the na-tion, Great of heart and great of mind.

Dick Whittington[1]

Ethel Crowninshield

Welsh Folk Tune

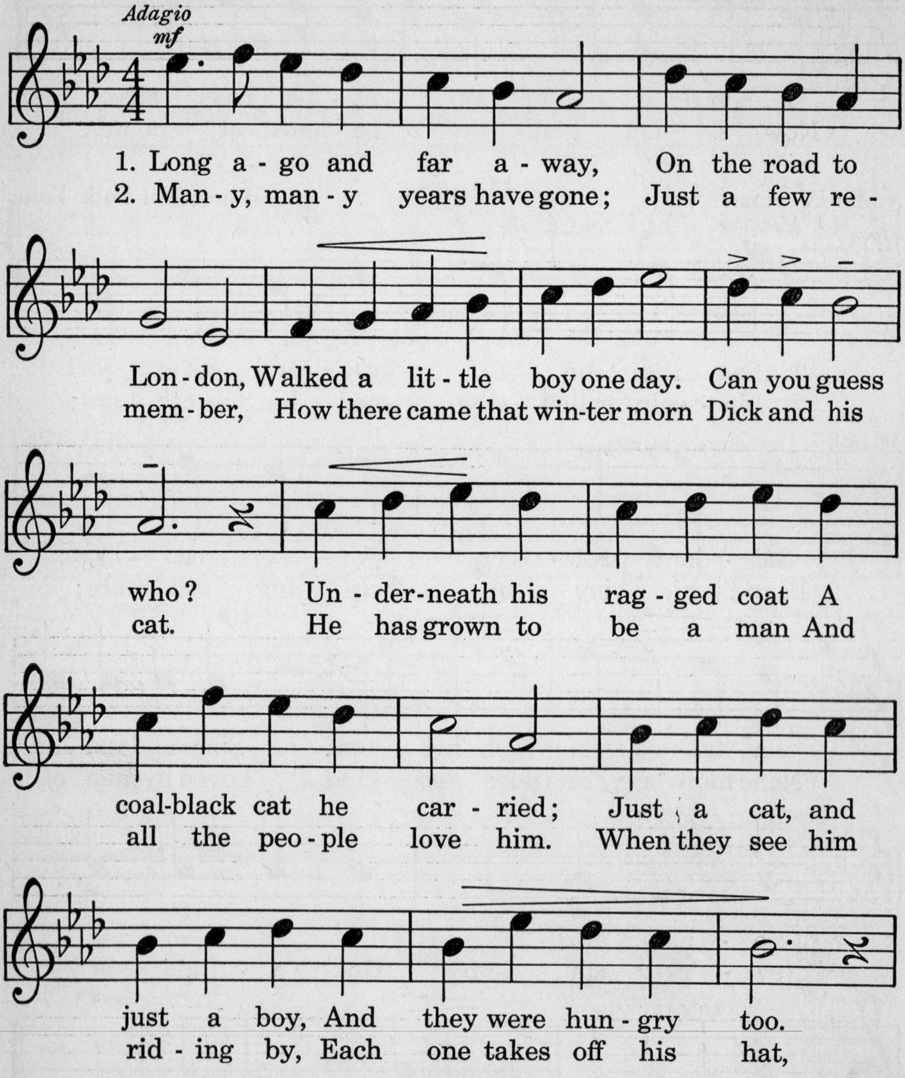
Adagio
mf
1. Long a - go and far a - way, On the road to
2. Man - y, man - y years have gone; Just a few re -
Lon - don, Walked a lit - tle boy one day. Can you guess
mem - ber, How there came that win-ter morn Dick and his
who? Un - der-neath his rag - ged coat A
cat. He has grown to be a man And
coal-black cat he car - ried; Just a cat, and
all the peo - ple love him. When they see him
just a boy, And they were hun - gry too.
rid - ing by, Each one takes off his hat,

[1] Dick Whittington was an English country lad. He came to London with his only friend and possession, a cat. He became successful and wealthy and was Lord Mayor of London three times.

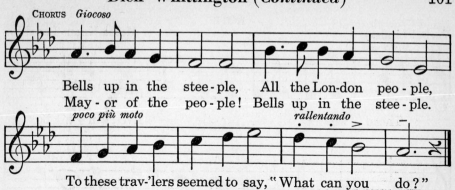

CHORUS *Giocoso*

Bells up in the stee - ple, All the Lon-don peo - ple,
May - or of the peo - ple! Bells up in the stee - ple.

poco più moto *rallentando*

To these trav-'lers seemed to say, " What can you do ? "
Nev - er rung for an - y-thing Strang - er than that.

The Herdboy

Blanche Jennings Thompson — Swiss Folk Tune

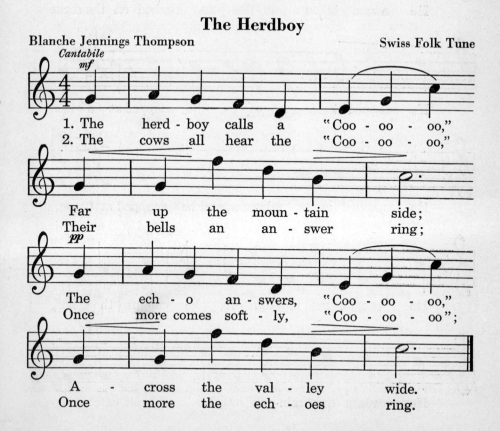

Cantabile
mf

1. The herd - boy calls a "Coo - oo - oo,"
2. The cows all hear the "Coo - oo - oo,"

Far up the moun - tain side;
Their bells an an - swer ring;

pp

The ech - o an - swers, "Coo - oo - oo,"
Once more comes soft - ly, "Coo - oo - oo";

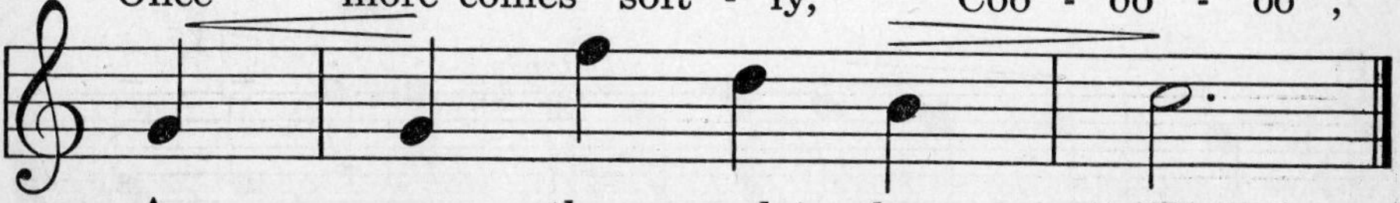

A - cross the val - ley wide.
Once more the ech - oes ring.

The Little Turtle

ROTE

Vachel Lindsay — Melba Knaus Loughlin

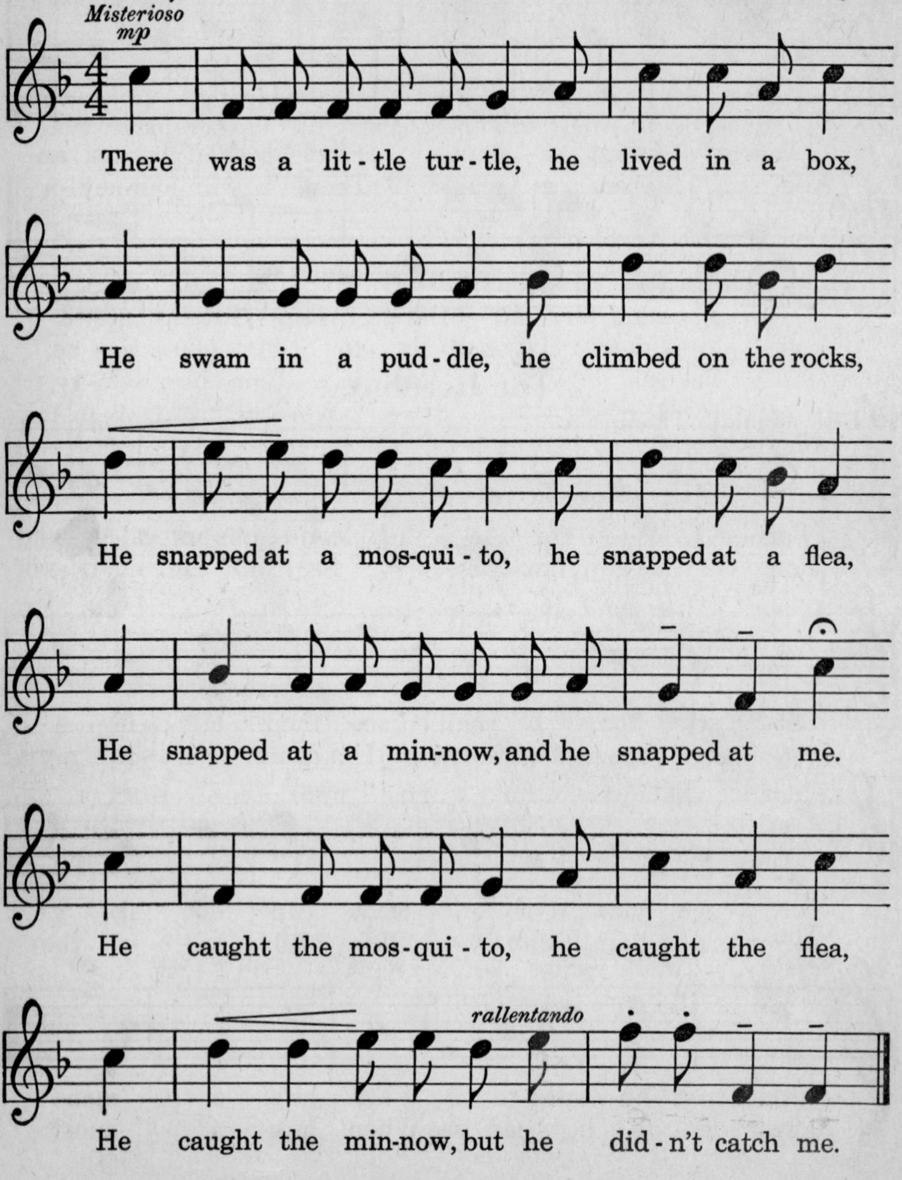
Misterioso
mp
There was a lit - tle tur - tle, he lived in a box,
He swam in a pud - dle, he climbed on the rocks,
He snapped at a mos-qui - to, he snapped at a flea,
He snapped at a min-now, and he snapped at me.
He caught the mos - qui - to, he caught the flea,
rallentando
He caught the min-now, but he did - n't catch me.

When I Am a Man

ROTE

Harvey Officer

Danish Folk Tune

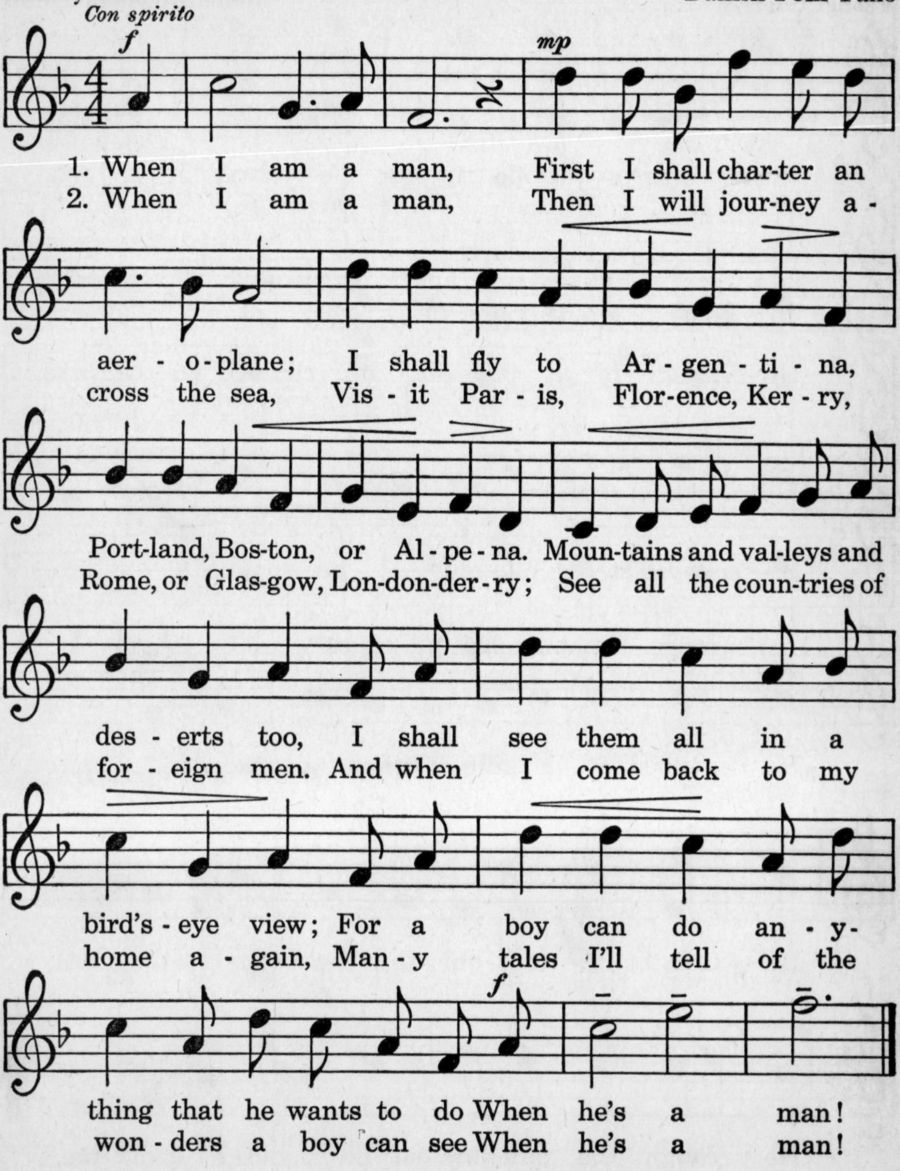
Con spirito
f
mp
1. When I am a man, First I shall char-ter an
2. When I am a man, Then I will jour-ney a -
aer - o - plane; I shall fly to Ar - gen - ti - na,
cross the sea, Vis - it Par - is, Flor-ence, Ker - ry,
Port-land, Bos-ton, or Al - pe - na. Moun-tains and val-leys and
Rome, or Glas-gow, Lon-don-der - ry; See all the coun-tries of
des - erts too, I shall see them all in a
for - eign men. And when I come back to my
bird's - eye view; For a boy can do an - y -
home a - gain, Man - y tales I'll tell of the
f
thing that he wants to do When he's a man!
won - ders a boy can see When he's a man!

Day Dreams

Marjorie Knapp — Wolfgang Amadeus Mozart

Dolce con espressione

1. Some - times on a sun - ny day
2. By the fire - light's pleas - ant glow,

Skies are laugh - ing and bright and blue;
In - doors, out - doors, or dark or fair,

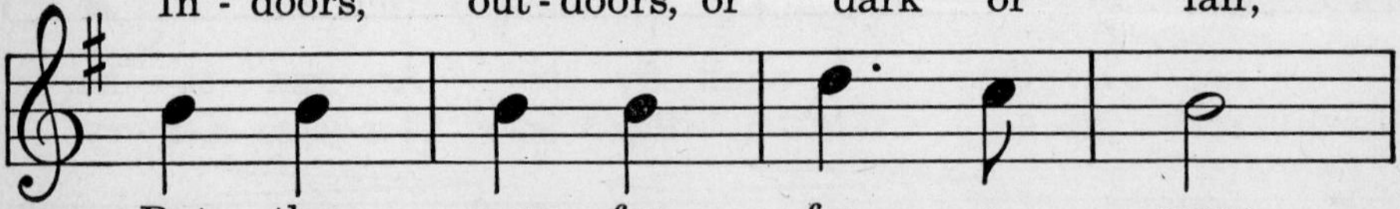

But they seem far, far a - way;
With the flow'rs or with the snow

Then strange dreams come to vis - it you.
Hap - py dreams may come an - y - where.

My Top

Mary C. Gleitz — Wendish Folk Tune

Allegretto

1. I've a top of red, green, and blue;
2. When the string is wound, let it go

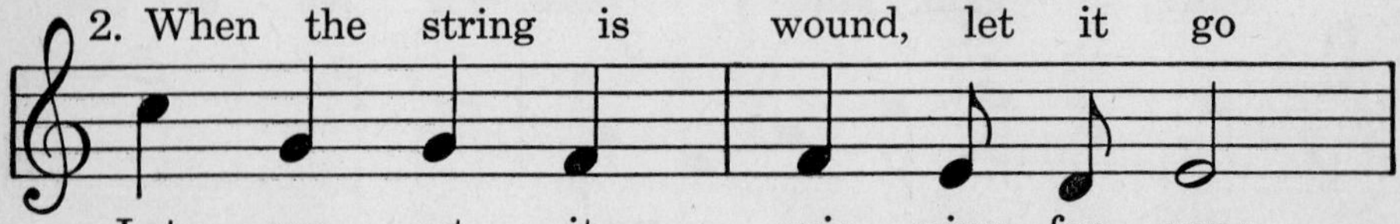

Let me set it spin - ning for you;
Danc - ing on its one lit - tle toe!

f
See it go a - round, rum - tum - tum!
See it go a - round, rum - tum - tum!
p
Hear it sing - ing, "Hum - hum - hum."
Hear it sing - ing, "Hum - hum - hum."

English version by
Frances Ford

Alpine Shepherds

Swiss Folk Song

Cantabile
1. Where the clear wa - ter croons,
2. Where the blue shad - ow falls
Through the bright aft - er - noons,
Down the steep moun - tain walls,
Shep - herd lads mer - ri - ly
Shep - herd lads mer - ri - ly
mf
Pipe their sim - ple tunes.
Chant their sim - ple tunes.

Art Extension Press, Inc.

Dutch Interior

"Within her sunny little house Dame Hilda sits at home"
Painted by De Hooch

Dame Hilda

ROTE

Christine Turner Curtis

Dutch Folk Tune

Semplice
mp
1. With - in her sun - ny lit - tle house
2. The lit - tle panes are full of light;
Dame Hil - da sits at home. The room is qui - et
Each win - dow is a star. Dame Hil - da's cap is
as a mouse. Down the street the chil - dren come.
snow - y white. Now she hears a tune a - far.
poco più moto
Hop, hop, bound! By tu - lip beds in pinks and blues;
Pure, like bells, Their voic - es ris - ing sweet and strong,
Tap, tap, sound The heels of their wood - en shoes.
Love - ly swells The mu - sic of chil-dren's song.

Warm Boots

Philip Muzzy

Russian Folk Tune

Animato
mf
1. See how the snow is fall - ing!
2. Sleighs on the ice are slid - ing;
Sleigh bells are call - ing;
Who is that glid - ing?
Bring me my coat and my boots trimmed with fur!
Old lone-some wolf, I can see you, sly sir.
I will stamp hard and show you
You have put on your coat and
My boots trimmed with fur.
Your boots trimmed with fur.

Just Suppose

ROTE

Mabel Livingstone

Jacques Wolfe

Giocoso
mp
1. Sup - pose the Old Wom-an who lived in a shoe And the
2. Sup - pose that the Cow who jumped o - ver the moon And the
Cat and the Fid - dle and Lit - tle Boy Blue, And
fun - ny round Dish that ran off with the Spoon, The
all the strange crea-tures in Moth - er Goose Rimes Should
Wom - an who sailed in a bas - ket so high Should
come out a - live and have vis - it-ing times—Just sup - pose!
knock at the door right this
Just sup - pose! Just sup - pose!
min-ute, oh my!
meno mosso
f
p
Just sup-pose! Just sup-pose! Just sup - pose!

Down the Road

Marjorie Knapp

Polish Folk Tune

Marcato
f
1. Down the road the scouts are march - ing;
2. Ev - 'ry - where the scouts are march - ing,
See their knap-sacks swing-ing! See their neck - er -
Mod-ern knights in train-ing; Faith - ful to their
chiefs, bright-col-ored, Hear their laugh - ter ring - ing!
drills and con-tests, Skill and wis - dom gain - ing.
March - ing to the wood - land, To
Brave and al - ways read - y, In
make their camp - fires rud - dy, O - ver hill and
dan - ger, help - ing oth - ers, Lov - ing flag and
val - ley, All na - ture for their stud - y.
coun - try, But call - ing all men broth - ers.

Laughing Lisa

English version by
Christine Turner Curtis

French-Canadian Folk Song

Con grazia
mf
1. Up - on the flow-'ry mead-ow Pret - ty Li - sa goes,
2 A - mid the wav - ing grass-es, Bloom-ing all a - part,
3. "Sweet dai - sy, if he loves me, An - swer me and tell:"
A twin - kle in her laugh-ter, Twin-kles in her toes.
She picks a snow-white dai - sy With a yel - low heart.
She pulls the dai - sy pet - als; Yes, he loves her well!
CHORUS leggiero
Sing tra la la la, sing tra la la la!
Tra la la la la, sing tra la la!
Sing tra la la la, sing tra la la la!
Tra la la la la la la!

The Deserted Farm

Carol Fuller

Robert Schumann

Lento
mp
1. No one talk - ing, no one walk - ing
2. Oh, I won - der, oh, I won - der!
Through this house so · quaint and dear.
May - be this last · rose would know
Why did all your friends for - sake you,
What be - came of all the chil - dren,
Leave you stand - ing · emp - ty here?
Play - ing here long · years a - go.

On the Mountain

English version by
Rose Fyleman

Norwegian Folk Song

Giocoso
mf
1. High a - bove the val - ley
2. Qui - et are the moun - tains,
I watch my herd of peace - ful kine,
And love - ly is the chang - ing sky;

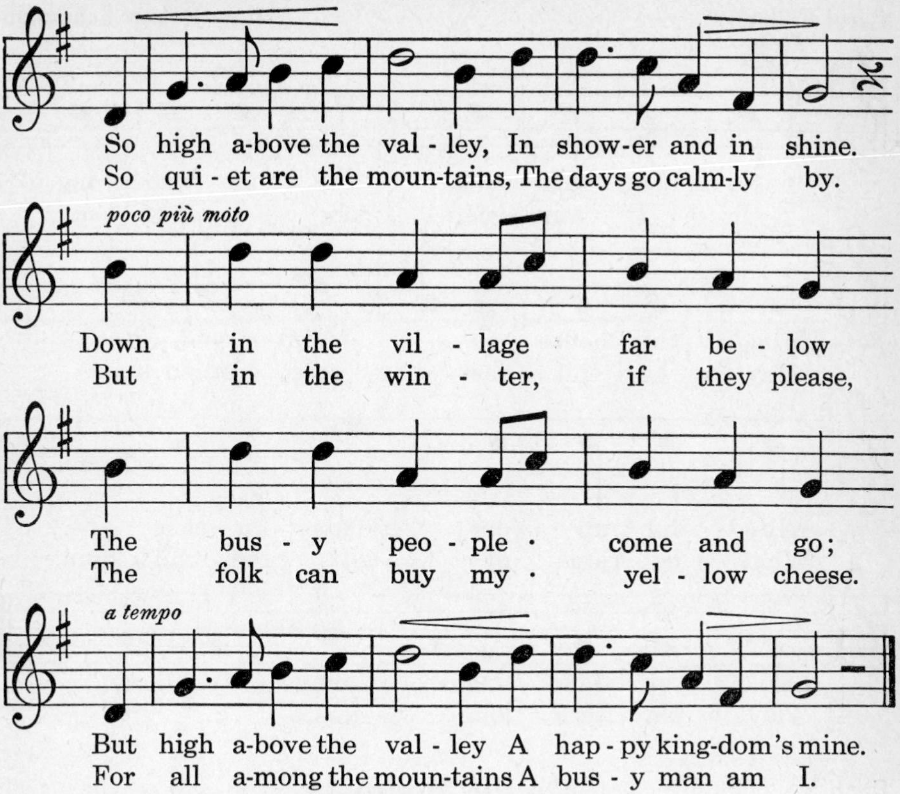
So high a-bove the val - ley, In show-er and in shine.
So qui - et are the moun-tains, The days go calm-ly by.
poco più moto
Down in the vil - lage far be - low
But in the win - ter, if they please,
The bus - y peo - ple · come and go;
The folk can buy my · yel - low cheese.
a tempo
But high a-bove the val - ley A hap - py king-dom's mine.
For all a-mong the moun-tains A bus - y man am I.

The Indian Brave

Virginia Lynd Hartley — American Indian Melody

Con espressione

mp

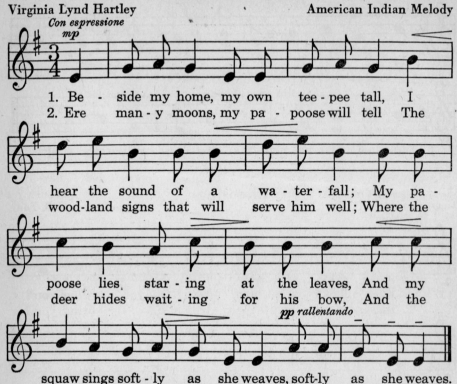

1\. Be - side my home, my own tee - pee tall, I
2\. Ere man - y moons, my pa - poose will tell The

hear the sound of a wa - ter - fall; My pa -
wood-land signs that will serve him well; Where the

poose lies star - ing at the leaves, And my
deer hides wait - ing for his bow, And the

pp rallentando

squaw sings soft - ly as she weaves, soft-ly as she weaves.
bear goes track-ing through the snow, track-ing through the snow.

English version by Louise Ayres Garnett

Marching Together

Swiss Folk Song

Ben marcato

f

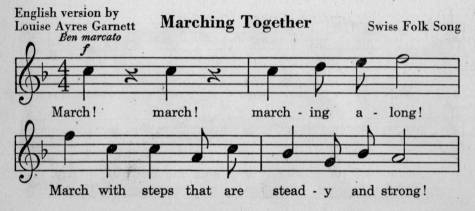

March! march! march - ing a - long!

March with steps that are stead - y and strong!

See how our flag in the sun - light is wav - ing,
Voic - es ring as now we sing our coun - try's song!

After the original by
Cecil Cowdrey

Choosing

Yugoslavian Folk Song

Giojoso
mf
1. Fine silk or sat - in, which may I bring you?
2. Red rose or white rose, which may I bring you?
Hey - fol - de - rol, hey - fol - de - rey!
Hey - fol - de - rol, hey - fol - de - rey!
Fine silk or sat - in, I will not choose them.
Red rose or white rose, I will not choose them.
Bring me a bird, a sing - ing bird to - day.
Bring me a ring, a ru - by ring to - day.

Spring Plowing

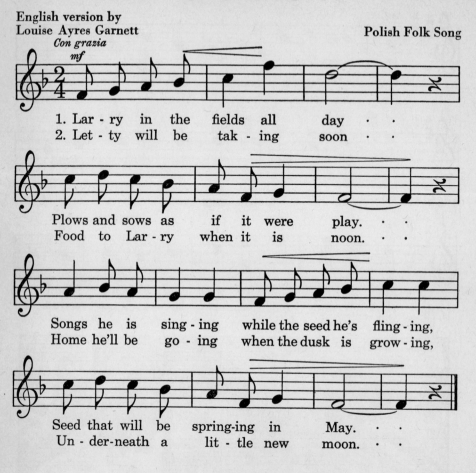

English version by
Louise Ayres Garnett

Polish Folk Song

Con grazia

1. Lar - ry in the fields all day . .
2. Let - ty will be tak - ing soon . .

Plows and sows as if it were play. . .
Food to Lar - ry when it is noon. . .

Songs he is sing - ing while the seed he's fling - ing,
Home he'll be go - ing when the dusk is grow - ing,

Seed that will be spring-ing in May. . .
Un - der-neath a lit - tle new moon. . .

On the Merry-go-round

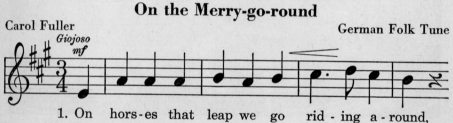

Carol Fuller

German Folk Tune

Giojoso

1. On hors-es that leap we go rid - ing a - round,
2. Oh, your horse is hand-some, he goes with a bound;

p
Go rid - ing a - round. Hur - ry up, take the
He goes with a bound. Mine is quite a large
bay one, or jump on the gray one! The
li - on, so please keep your eye on My
f
mu - sic is mak - ing a gal - lop - ing sound.
li - on and me, on our mer - ry - go - round.

Quiet Night

Susanna Myers — Spanish Folk Tune

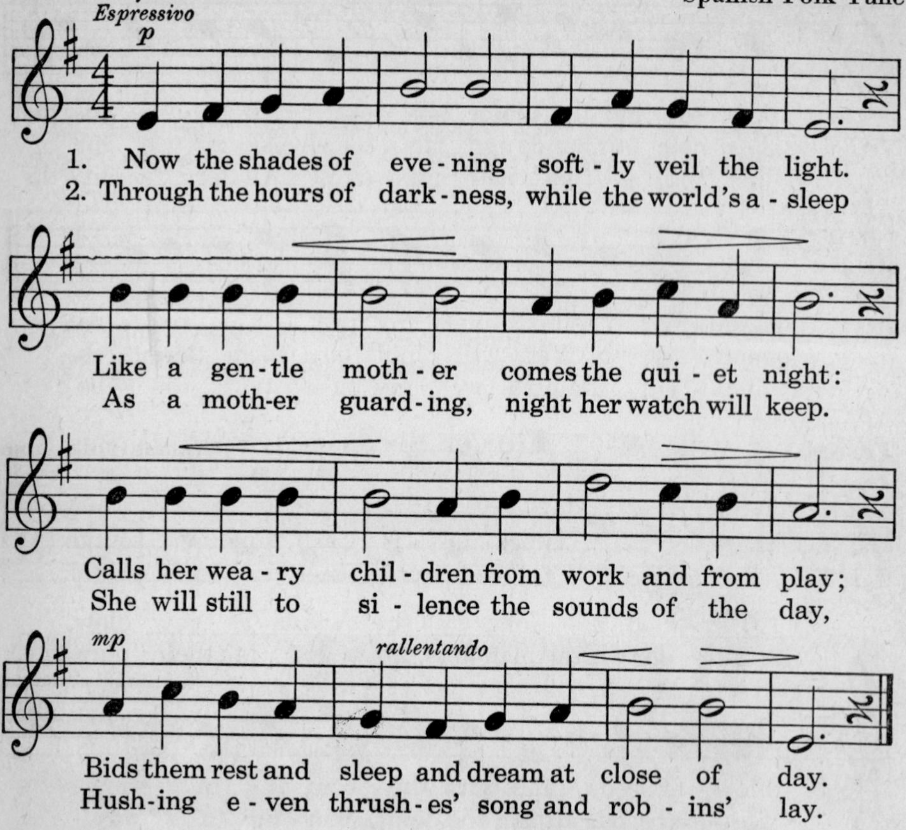
Espressivo
p
1. Now the shades of eve-ning soft-ly veil the light.
2. Through the hours of dark-ness, while the world's a-sleep
Like a gen-tle moth-er comes the qui-et night:
As a moth-er guard-ing, night her watch will keep.
Calls her wea-ry chil-dren from work and from play;
She will still to si-lence the sounds of the day,
mp
rallentando
Bids them rest and sleep and dream at close of day.
Hush-ing e-ven thrush-es' song and rob-ins' lay.

Who'll Buy?

Eleanor Farjeon — ROTE — Polish Folk Tune

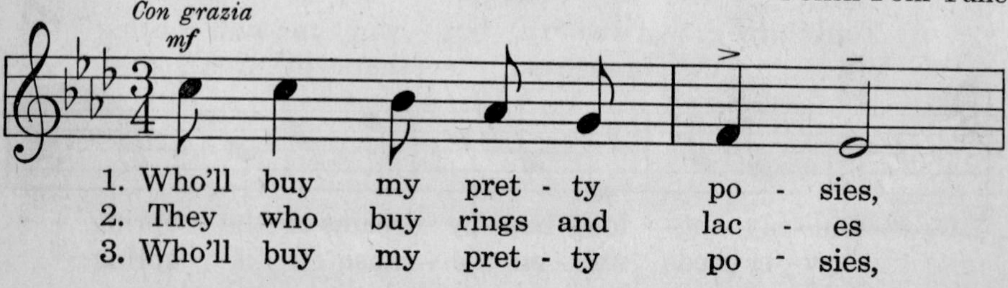
Con grazia
mf
1. Who'll buy my pret-ty po-sies,
2. They who buy rings and lac-es
3. Who'll buy my pret-ty po-sies,

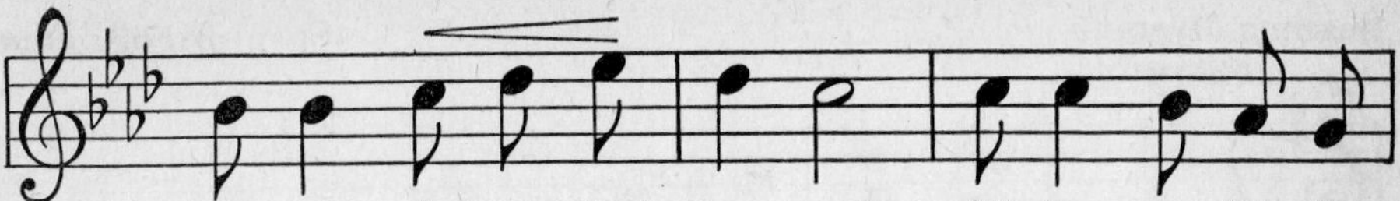

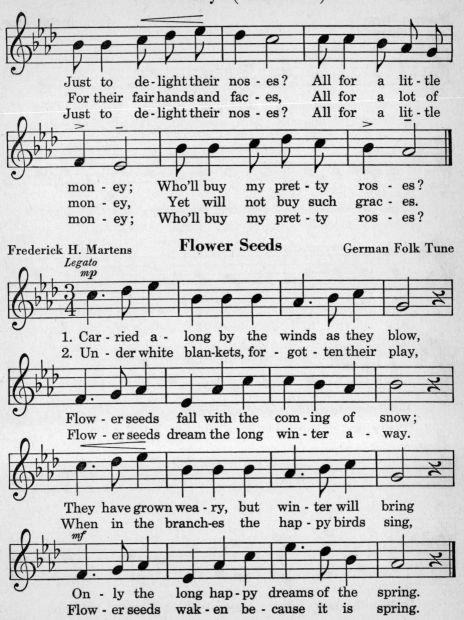

Just to de-light their nos - es? All for a lit - tle
For their fair hands and fac - es, All for a lot of
Just to de-light their nos - es? All for a lit - tle

mon - ey; Who'll buy my pret - ty ros - es?
mon - ey, Yet will not buy such grac - es.
mon - ey; Who'll buy my pret - ty ros - es?

Flower Seeds

Frederick H. Martens German Folk Tune

1. Car - ried a - long by the winds as they blow,
2. Un - der white blan-kets, for - got - ten their play,

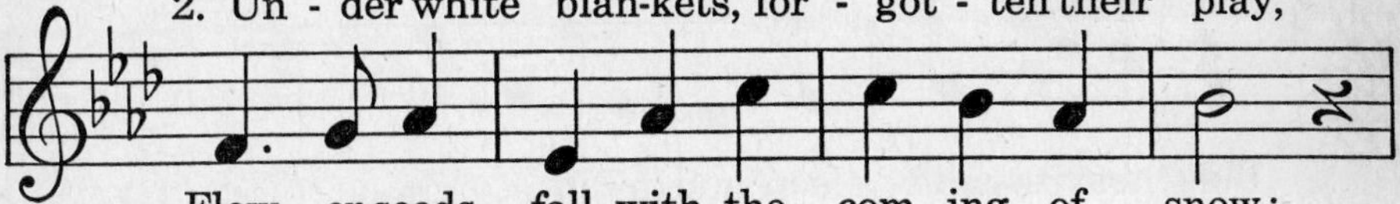

Flow - er seeds fall with the com - ing of snow;
Flow - er seeds dream the long win - ter a - way.

They have grown wea - ry, but win - ter will bring
When in the branch-es the hap - py birds sing,

On - ly the long hap - py dreams of the spring.
Flow - er seeds wak - en be - cause it is spring.

Queer Facts

Mabel Livingstone — Mana-Zucca

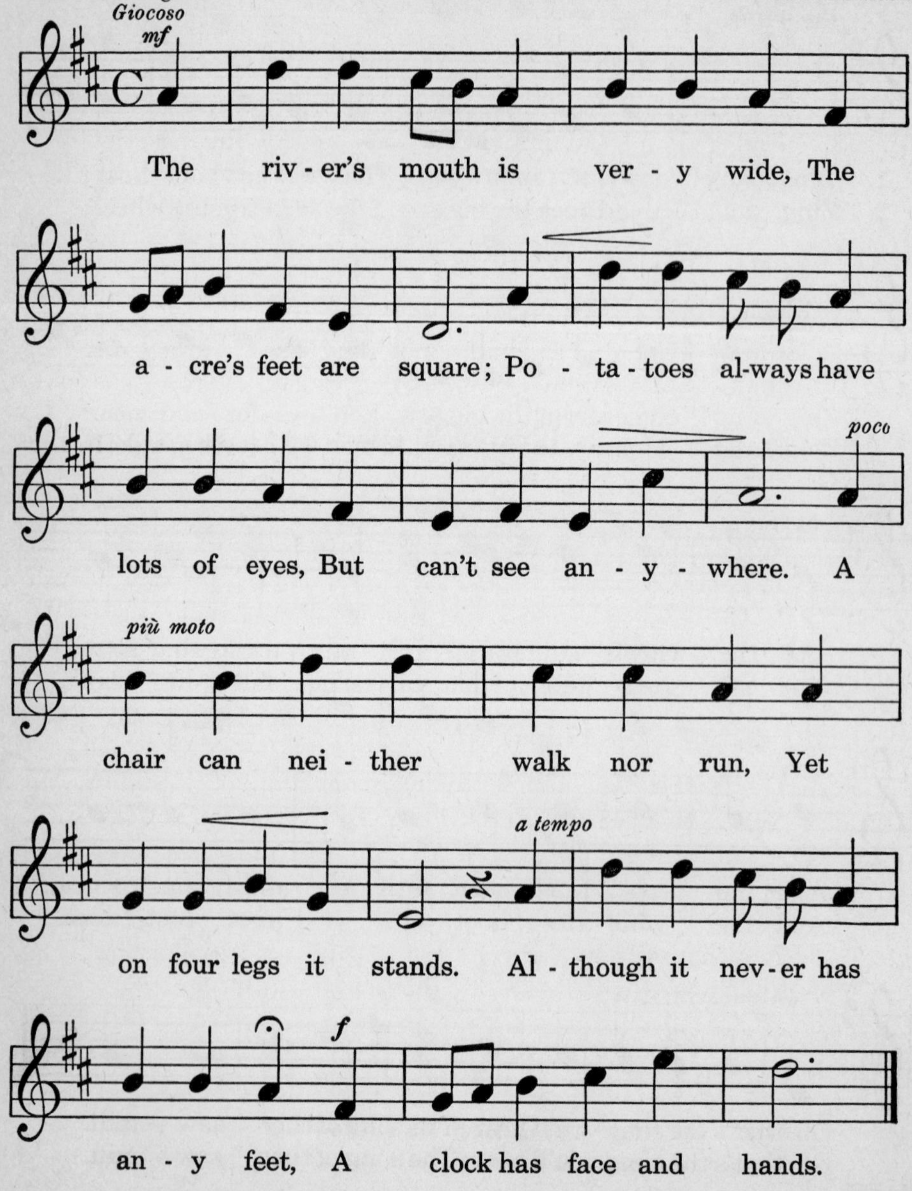
Giocoso
mf
The riv-er's mouth is ver-y wide, The
a-cre's feet are square; Po-ta-toes al-ways have
lots of eyes, But can't see an-y-where. A
poco
più moto
chair can nei-ther walk nor run, Yet
on four legs it stands. Al-though it nev-er has
a tempo
an-y feet, A clock has face and hands.
f

The Sawmill

Josephine Royle | German Folk Tune

Con spirito

1. "Bing, bang!" down at the saw-mill, That is what you hear;
2. "Zing, zang!" round goes the big saw, Like a gleam-ing wheel;

"Zing, zang!" comes from the big saw, Ech-oes far and near.
"Zing, zang!" look at the big saw, Armed with teeth of steel!

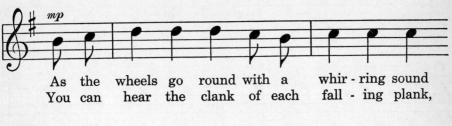

As the wheels go round with a whir-ring sound
You can hear the clank of each fall-ing plank,

And the pis-tons push with a shush, shush, shush,
And the whis-tles hoot with a toot, toot, toot.

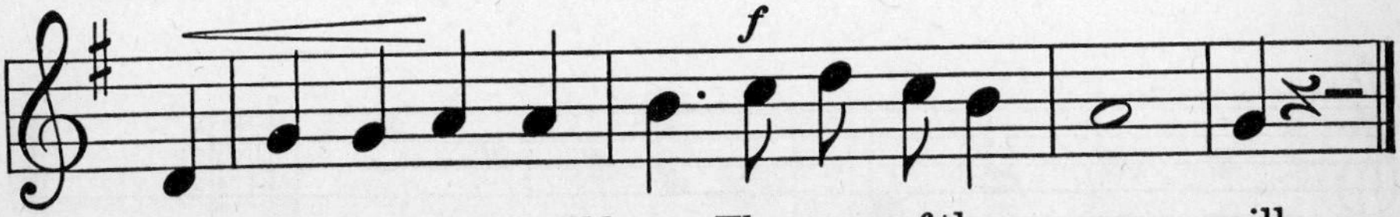

Oh, that's the song you'll hear; The song of the saw-mill.
Oh, that's the song you'll hear; The song of the saw-mill.

The Pipers of Balmoral

After the original by
Marjorie Knapp

Scotch Folk Song

Allegretto
mp
1. At the foot of Craig Gow - an, And by
2. With the fern and the hare - bell All the
3. Roy - al home in the high - lands, From a-
Dee's wa - ters clear, Stands the cas - tle Bal - mor - al
wood-land is clad, And the stur - dy Scotch pip - ers
far we may see How you shine in the sun - light
With the pines sing - ing near.
Are in kilt of the plaid.
On the banks of the Dee!
Chorus
O Bal - mor - al, Bal -
mor - al, With your tur - rets gleam-ing white! With our
mf
bag-pipes we'll praise you, Both by day and by night.

The Art Extension Press, Inc.

The Pipers of Balmoral

Painted by the American artist GARI MELCHERS

May Breezes

Susanna Myers | Danish Melody

Cantabile
mp
1. The per - fume of the spring - time
2. A thou - sand, thou - sand blos - soms
Is in the balm - y air; The
Are blown up - on the breeze; The
scent of li - lacs, hon - ey sweet, And ap - ple blos-soms
drift - ing pet - als, white as snow, Float through the air, as
mf
spic - y sweet And count-less flow - ers fair. In
light as snow, A - mong the or - chard trees. In
mf
May - time, in May - time, The gen - tle breez-es blow, All
May - time, in May - time, The gen - tle breez-es blow, All
lad - en with fra - grance Where love-ly gar-dens grow.
lad - en with fra - grance Where love-ly gar-dens grow.

Spring Messengers

Clara Louise Kessler — Russian Folk Tune

Grazioso
p
1. Wind in the ce - dar tree,
2. Bird in the sun - ny sky,
Wind ev - er flow - ing free,
Bird fly - ing slow - ly by,
What are you hum - ming?
Where are you wing - ing?
Whis - per your song to me.
Come to my ce - dar tree.
mf
"Spring - time is com - ing,
Branch - es are swing - ing,
Spring - time is com - ing."
Breez - es are sing - ing.

Juliska[1]

Carol Fuller — Hungarian Folk Tune

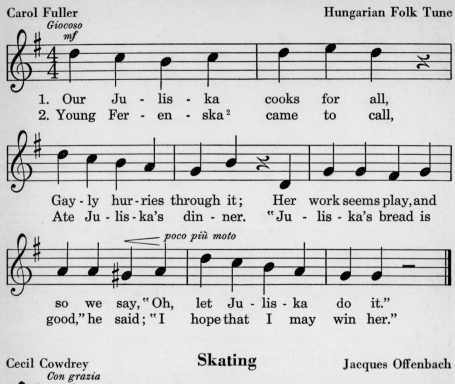

1. Our Ju - lis - ka cooks for all,
2. Young Fer - en - ska[2] came to call,

Gay - ly hur - ries through it; Her work seems play, and
Ate Ju - lis - ka's din - ner. "Ju - lis - ka's bread is

so we say, "Oh, let Ju - lis - ka do it."
good," he said; "I hope that I may win her."

Skating

Cecil Cowdrey — Jacques Offenbach

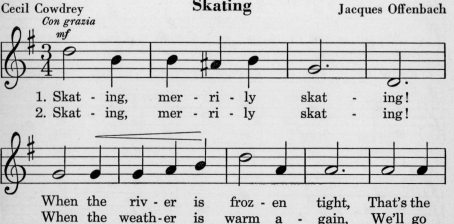

1. Skat - ing, mer - ri - ly skat - ing!
2. Skat - ing, mer - ri - ly skat - ing!

When the riv - er is froz - en tight, That's the
When the weath - er is warm a - gain, We'll go

[1] Pronounced "yu lish′ka." [2] Pronounced "fer en′shka."

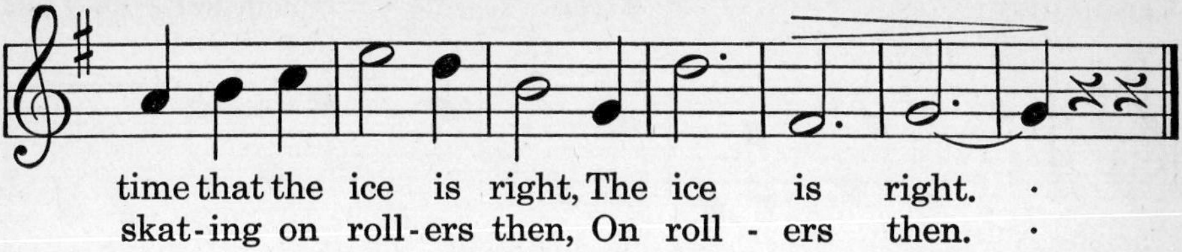
time that the ice is right, The ice is right.
skat-ing on roll-ers then, On roll - ers then.

Cobweb Cradles

Clara Edwards Clara Edwards

Dolce
mp
One morn-ing ver - y ear - ly, Up in the cher-ry
trees, I saw some sil - ver cra - dles A -
swing-ing in the breeze. Now what did I find in them?
I'll whis-per it to you: 'Twas not a ti - ny
elf - in, But just a drop of dew.

April

Theodosia Garrison | ROTE | Bainbridge Crist

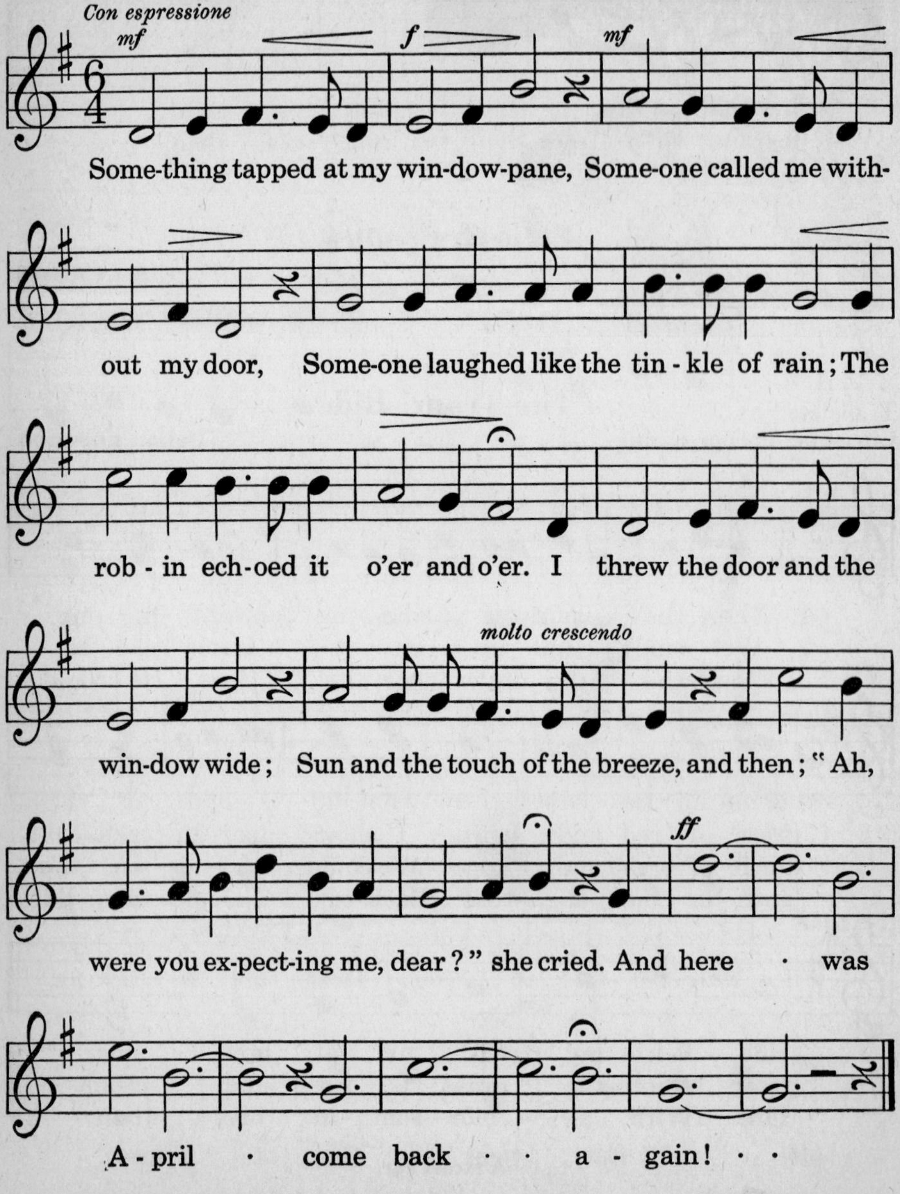
Con espressione
mf
f
mf
Some-thing tapped at my win-dow-pane, Some-one called me with-
out my door, Some-one laughed like the tin - kle of rain ; The
rob - in ech-oed it o'er and o'er. I threw the door and the
molto crescendo
win-dow wide ; Sun and the touch of the breeze, and then ; " Ah,
ff
were you ex-pect-ing me, dear ? " she cried. And here · was
A - pril · come back · · a - gain! · ·

The Tram[1] Ride

Translated by
Christine Turner Curtis

Italian Folk Song

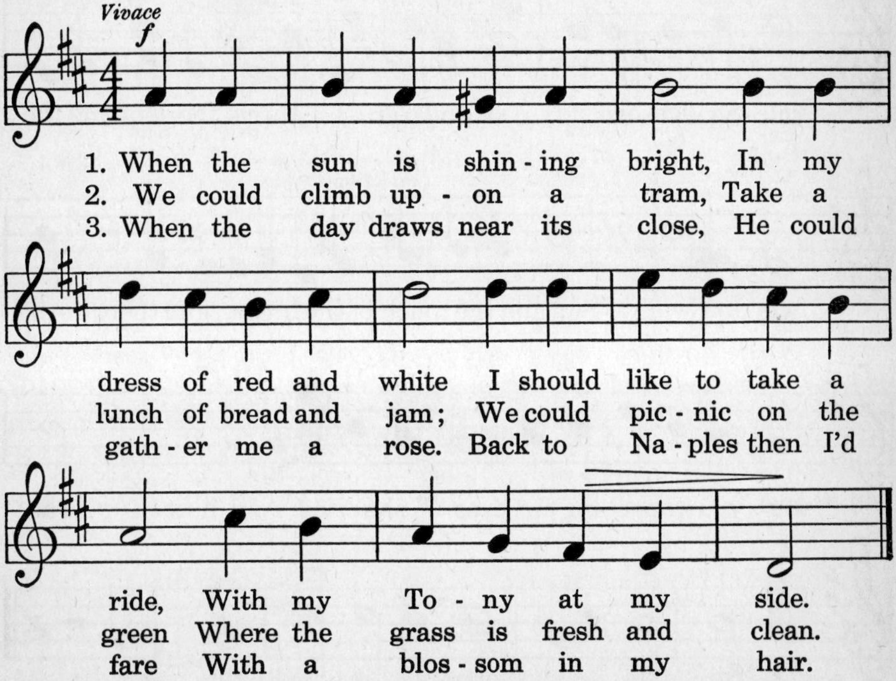
Vivace
1. When the sun is shin - ing bright, In my dress of red and white I should like to take a ride, With my To - ny at my side.
2. We could climb up - on a tram, Take a lunch of bread and jam; We could pic - nic on the green Where the grass is fresh and clean.
3. When the day draws near its close, He could gath - er me a rose. Back to Na - ples then I'd fare With a blos - som in my hair.

[1] A street car.

Our Land

English version by
Ethel Crowninshield

Bulgarian Folk Song

Maestoso
mf
1. Land of the moun-tains, land of the riv - ers,
2. Hearts that are hap - py, hands that are will - ing,
Land where the sea rolls in from east and west:
Each day will find some use - ful work to do.
f
All your beau - ty, free - ly do you give us.
Bus - y days with hap - pi - ness we're fill - ing;
meno mosso
Here is our song, O land, we love the best!
We'll do our best, our na - tive land, for you!

The Man in the Moon

ROTE

Old Rhyme

Geoffrey O'Hara

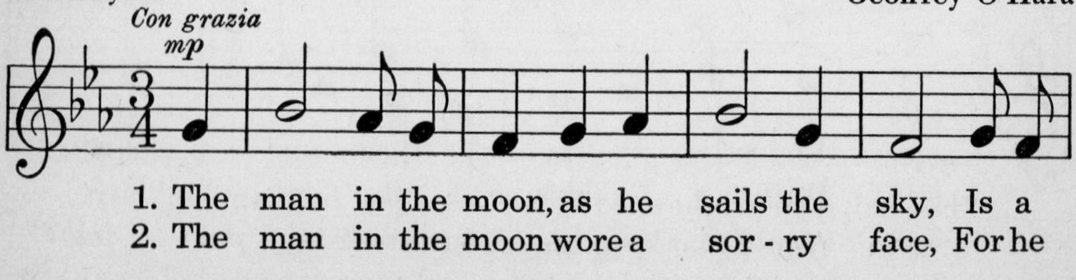
Con grazia
mp
1. The man in the moon, as he sails the sky, Is a
2. The man in the moon wore a sor - ry face, For he

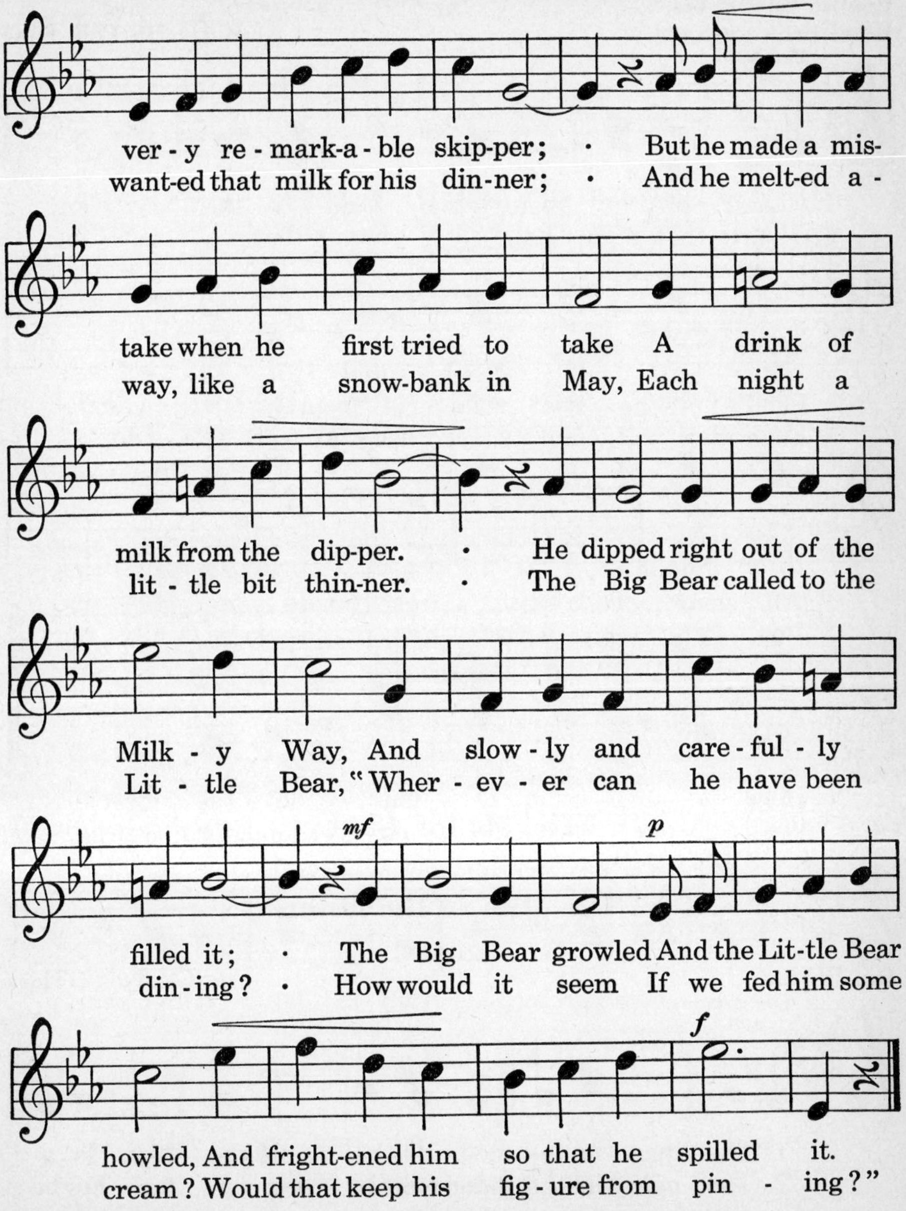
ver - y re - mark-a - ble skip-per; · But he made a mis-
want-ed that milk for his din-ner; · And he melt-ed a -
take when he first tried to take A drink of
way, like a snow-bank in May, Each night a
milk from the dip-per. · He dipped right out of the
lit - tle bit thin-ner. · The Big Bear called to the
Milk - y Way, And slow - ly and care - ful - ly
Lit - tle Bear, " Wher - ev - er can he have been
mf
p
filled it; · The Big Bear growled And the Lit-tle Bear
din - ing? · How would it seem If we fed him some
f
howled, And fright-ened him so that he spilled it.
cream? Would that keep his fig - ure from pin - ing?"

The Fisherman's Wife

English version by
Hannah Bailey

Danish Folk Song

Sostenuto
mp
1. Why gaze you so sad-ly a-way to the sea? Moth-er, tell your sor-row to me. The wa-ter is blue and the sand-pip-ers sing, And fish-er-men's boats are de-part-ing.
2. Why look you so wild-ly a-way to the deep? Moth-er, tell me, why do you weep? The tem-pest is o-ver, a-gain the bells ring; But nev-er a boat is re-turn-ing.

Crickets for Luck

Translated by
Carol Fuller

Italian Folk Song

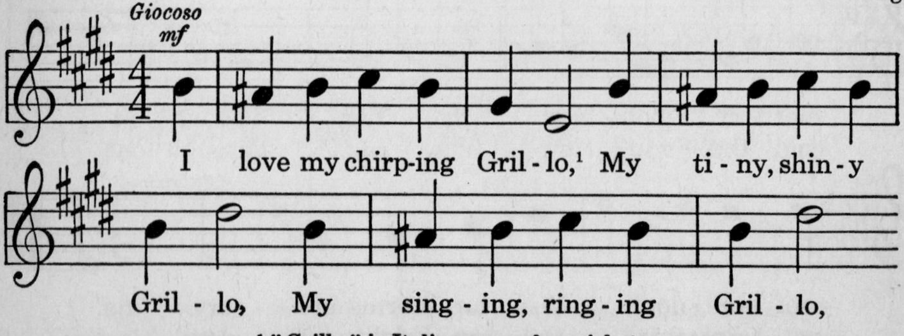
Giocoso
mf
I love my chirp-ing Gril-lo,[1] My ti-ny, shin-y Gril-lo, My sing-ing, ring-ing Gril-lo,

[1] "Grillo," is Italian name for cricket.

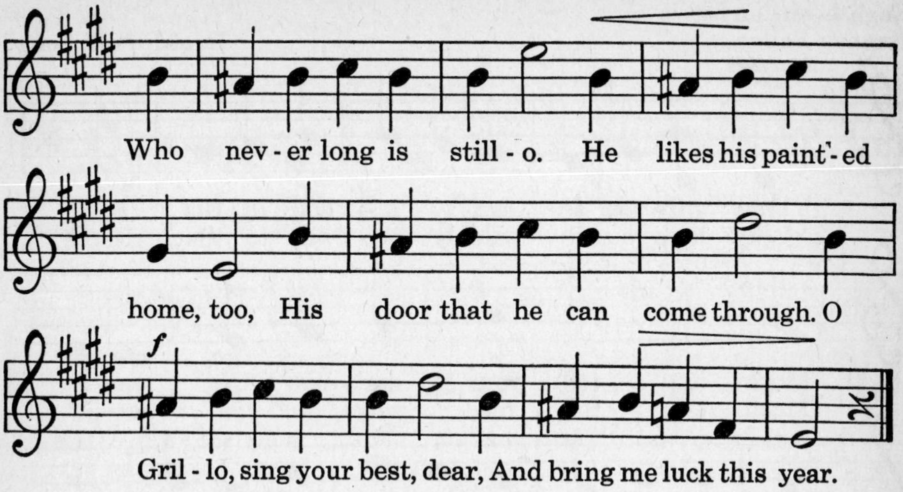
Who nev - er long is still - o. He likes his paint'- ed
home, too, His door that he can come through. O
f
Gril - lo, sing your best, dear, And bring me luck this year.

Weaving

English version by
Cecil Cowdrey

Lettish Folk Song

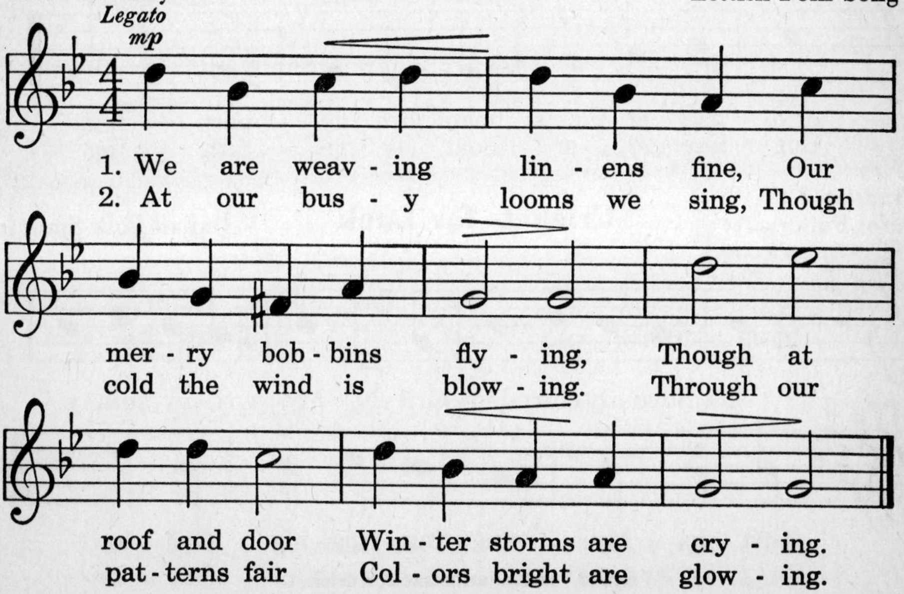
Legato
mp
1. We are weav - ing lin - ens fine, Our
2. At our bus - y looms we sing, Though
mer - ry bob - bins fly - ing, Though at
cold the wind is blow - ing. Through our
roof and door Win - ter storms are cry - ing.
pat - terns fair Col - ors bright are glow - ing.

Marching Song

Rose Fyleman

Danish Folk Tune

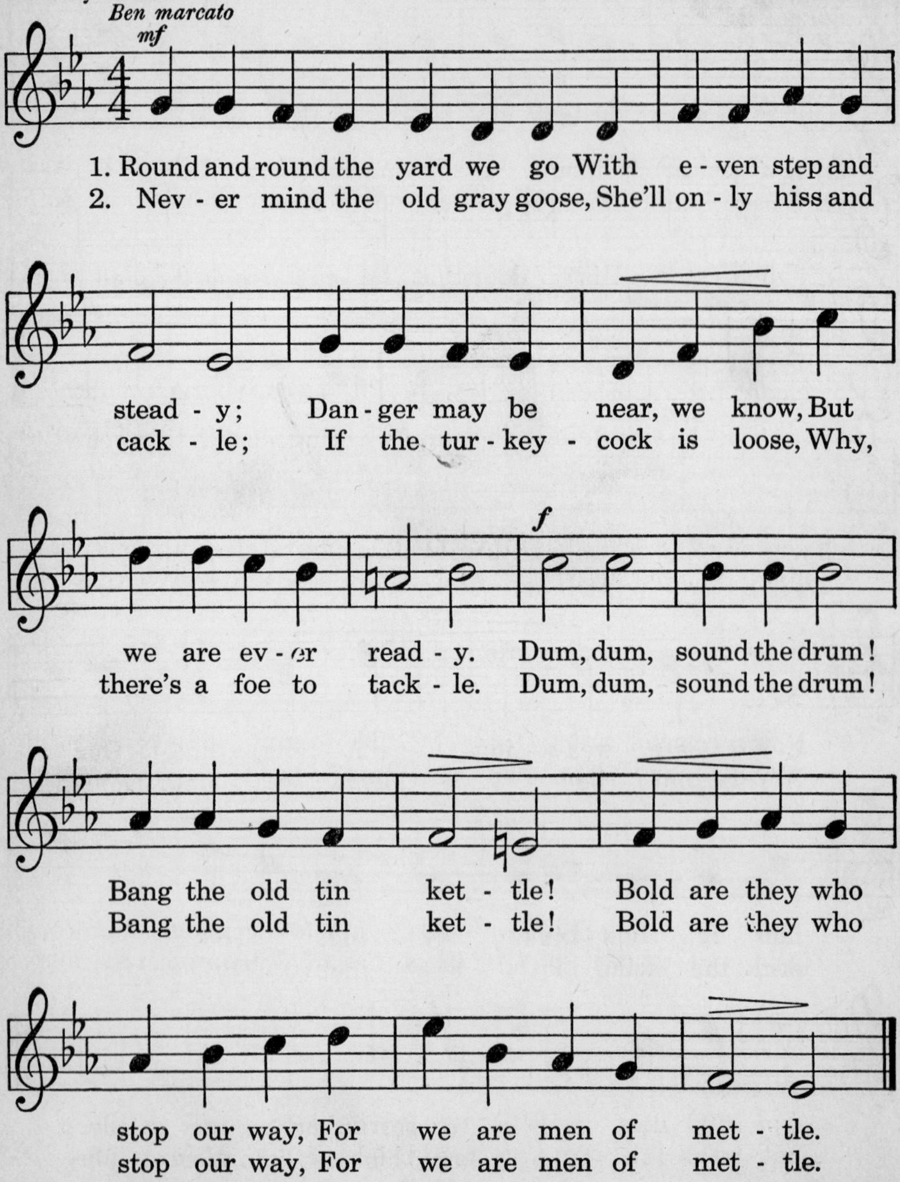
Ben marcato
mf
1. Round and round the yard we go With e - ven step and
2. Nev - er mind the old gray goose, She'll on - ly hiss and
stead - y; Dan - ger may be near, we know, But
cack - le; If the tur - key - cock is loose, Why,
f
we are ev - er read - y. Dum, dum, sound the drum!
there's a foe to tack - le. Dum, dum, sound the drum!
Bang the old tin ket - tle! Bold are they who
Bang the old tin ket - tle! Bold are they who
stop our way, For we are men of met - tle.
stop our way, For we are men of met - tle.

The Chimney Sweep

Translated by
Carol Fuller

ROTE

Italian Folk Song

Con moto
mf
1. Sweep your chim-ney, sweep your chim-ney! When I pass
2. Sweep your chim-ney, sweep your chim-ney! Brush it so
f
by, you hear my loud cry. I'll sweep your chim-ney!
clean no soot can be seen. I'll sweep your chim-ney,
sweep your chim-ney! Please let me come and clean up your home.
sweep your chim-ney! I nev-er shirk but do good hard work.
Now see how quick-ly I be - gin. Boys can jump
On - ly one trou - ble sets me back: I grow so
in be - cause they are thin. Wield-ing my broom through
black; my face is so black, Chil-dren are scared and
cin - ders deep, Help me to earn some cor-ner to sleep.
run a - way, When I should like to join them at play.

The Storm Winds

Christine Turner Curtis | Helen Sewall Leavitt

Con espressione
mf
1. High on the hill dark shad - ows pass,
2. High in the moon-light cir - cle they;
And whines the wind through frost - y grass;
The witch - es' hair is wild and gray.
poco più moto
The witch - es ride their brooms to - night
They mount the air, they ride the cloud,
A - cross the mead - ows cold and white.
Their laugh - ter ring - ing shrill and loud.
a tempo
Clear - ing the tree - tops, see them blow
Dark - ly they stream through win - ter skies,
f
rallentando
A-bove the wood-land, sail-ing in a long black row.
And all the mid-night ech-oes with their storm-y cries.

Boating

Maud W. Niedermeyer — Yugoslavian Folk Tune

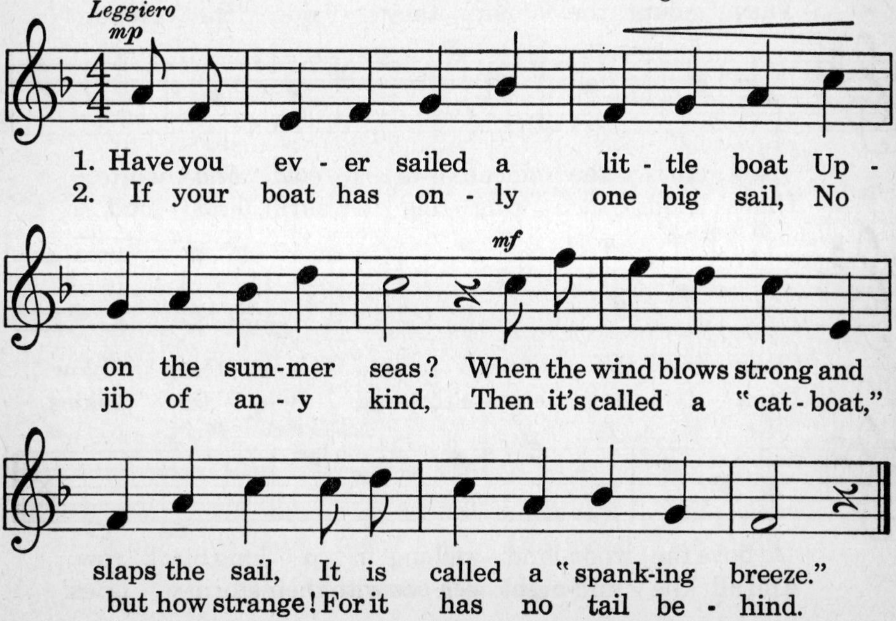
Leggiero
mp
1. Have you ev - er sailed a lit - tle boat Up - on the sum-mer seas? When the wind blows strong and slaps the sail, It is called a "spank-ing breeze."
2. If your boat has on - ly one big sail, No jib of an - y kind, Then it's called a "cat - boat," but how strange! For it has no tail be - hind.
mf

Sunny Naples

After the original by
Nellie Poorman

Italian Folk Song

Grazioso
mp
1. "O gay Na-po - li, · · sun - ny Na-po - li!" ·
2. "O gay Na-po - li, · · sun - ny Na-po - li!" ·
Says the mu - sic most en - tranc-ing! "Love - ly
Says the mu - sic most en - tranc-ing! "Love - ly
Na - po - li, · · queen - ly Na - po - li!" · ·
Na - po - li, · · queen - ly Na - po - li!" · ·
Says the tune the hur - dy-gur - dy plays. · ·
Says the tune the hur - dy-gur - dy plays. · ·
"Come, dance a - way the hap - py hours A - mid fair
"Come, broth - er Gian - ni,[1] mer - ry boy, And dark-eyed
Na - ples' fra - grant flow'rs, Be - side the sea whose
Ros - a, laugh with joy! What fun to dance on

[1] Pronounced "Jahn'ne."

mag - ic hue Can match the heav-en's own blue."
fly - ing feet In time with mel - o - dy sweet!"

Shadows

Louise Ayres Garnett — Polish Folk Tune

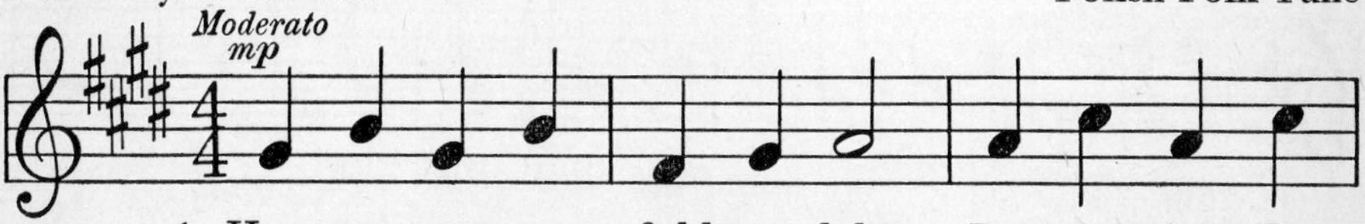

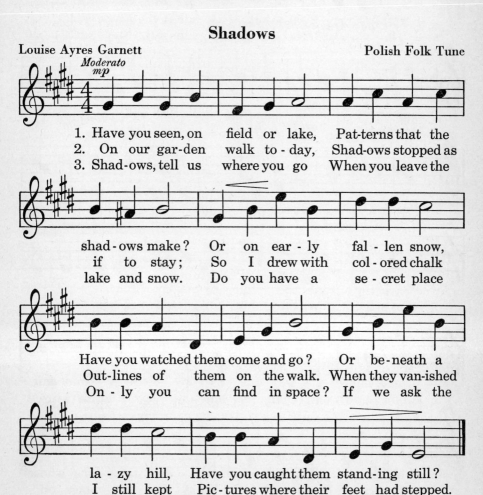

1. Have you seen, on field or lake, Pat-terns that the
2. On our gar-den walk to - day, Shad-ows stopped as
3. Shad-ows, tell us where you go When you leave the

shad - ows make? Or on ear - ly fal - len snow,
if to stay; So I drew with col - ored chalk
lake and snow. Do you have a se - cret place

Have you watched them come and go? Or be-neath a
Out-lines of them on the walk. When they van-ished
On - ly you can find in space? If we ask the

la - zy hill, Have you caught them stand-ing still?
I still kept Pic - tures where their feet had stepped.
moon and sun, They may tell us where you run.

Merrymaking

English version by
Christine Turner Curtis

Italian Folk Song

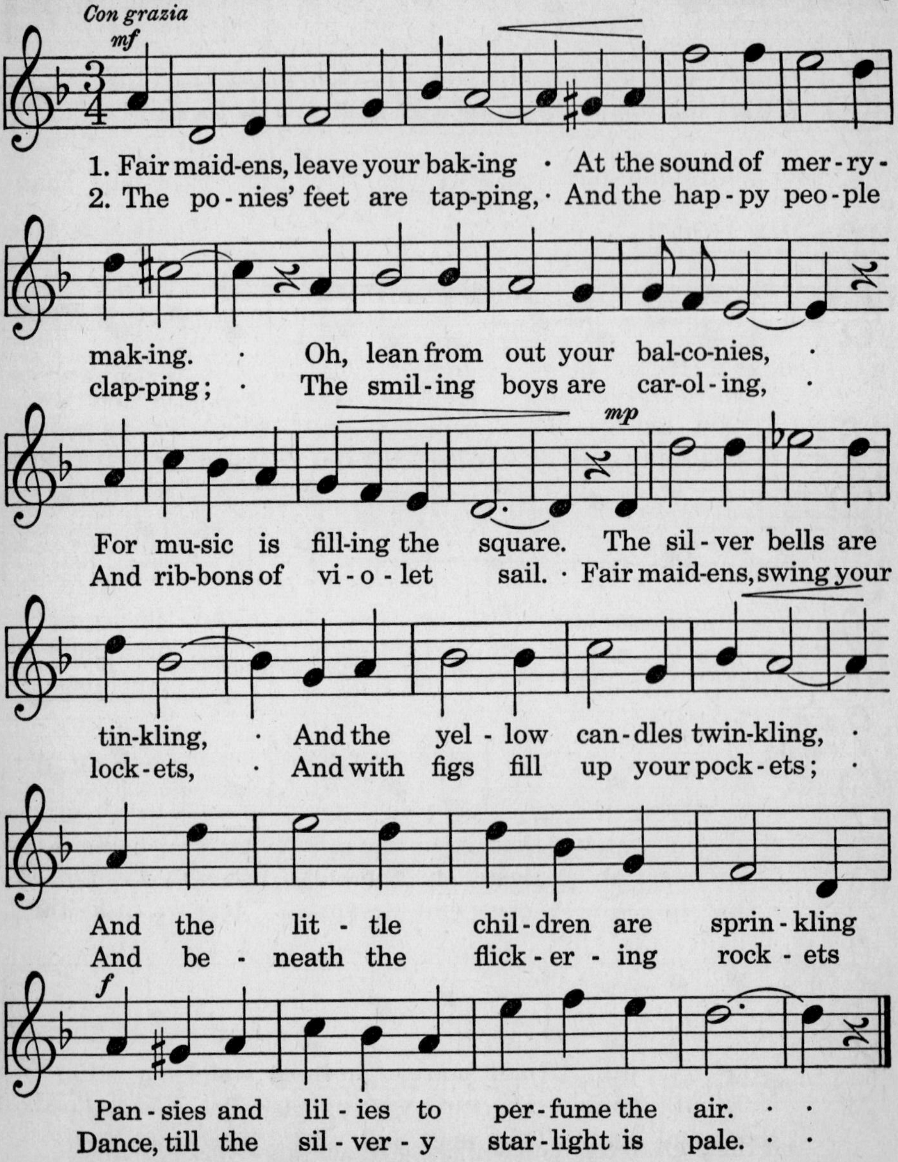
Con grazia
mf
1. Fair maid-ens, leave your bak-ing · At the sound of mer-ry-
2. The po-nies' feet are tap-ping, · And the hap-py peo-ple
mak-ing. · Oh, lean from out your bal-co-nies, ·
clap-ping; · The smil-ing boys are car-ol-ing, ·
mp
For mu-sic is fill-ing the square. The sil-ver bells are
And rib-bons of vi-o-let sail. · Fair maid-ens, swing your
tin-kling, · And the yel-low can-dles twin-kling, ·
lock-ets, · And with figs fill up your pock-ets; ·
And the lit-tle chil-dren are sprin-kling
And be-neath the flick-er-ing rock-ets
f
Pan-sies and lil-ies to per-fume the air. · ·
Dance, till the sil-ver-y star-light is pale. · ·

The Fountain

ROTE

Marjorie Knapp

Lily Strickland

Leggiero
p
The foun-tain is play-ing a sil - ver tune That
sings in the qui-et of night. The sky with its stars and its
shin - ing moon Has lent it a crys - tal
light. O mu - si - cal foun-tain, we love your song, We
mf
love your beau-ti - ful gleams; Oh tin - kle and twin-kle through-
out the night long; You will bring to us sil - ver dreams.

The Art Extension Press, Inc.

The Haymakers

Painted by the American artist THEODORE C. STEELE. It is now in a private collection

The Haymakers

Marjorie Knapp

Ukrainian Folk Tune

1. Come, boys, come, boys, let us be go - ing! In the fields the

2. Come, girls, come, girls, cheer you are bring-ing. Work moves swift-ly

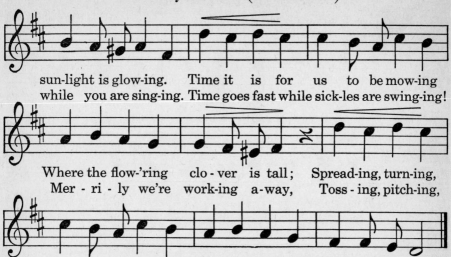

sun-light is glow-ing. Time it is for us to be mow-ing
while you are sing-ing. Time goes fast while sick-les are swing-ing!

Where the flow-'ring clo - ver is tall; Spread-ing, turn-ing,
Mer - ri - ly we're work-ing a-way, Toss - ing, pitch-ing,

rak - ing, and gath-'ring, While the sun shines bright on us all.
lift - ing, and load - ing, Pil - ing up the sweet-scent-ed hay.

Traveling

Susanna Myers

Danish Folk Tune

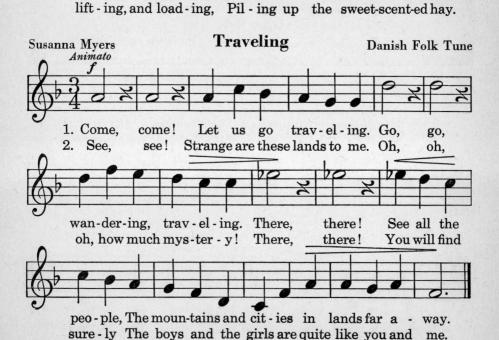

Animato

1. Come, come! Let us go trav - el - ing. Go, go,
2. See, see! Strange are these lands to me. Oh, oh,

wan-der-ing, trav - el - ing. There, there! See all the
oh, how much mys - ter - y! There, there! You will find

peo - ple, The moun-tains and cit - ies in lands far a - way.
sure - ly The boys and the girls are quite like you and me.

Westward

Derrick Norman Lehmer Collection

Chippewa Air

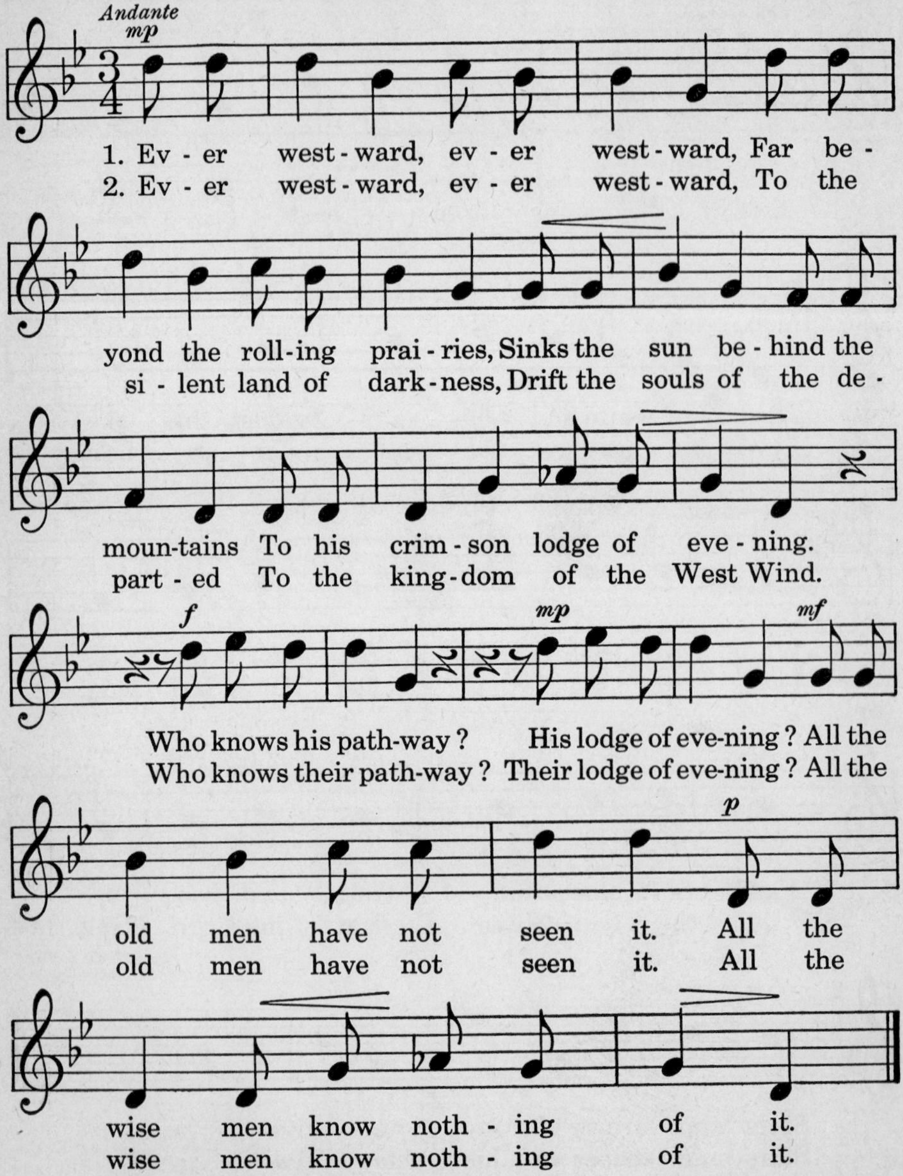
Andante
mp
1. Ev - er west - ward, ev - er west - ward, Far be - yond the roll - ing prai - ries, Sinks the sun be - hind the moun - tains To his crim - son lodge of eve - ning.
2. Ev - er west - ward, ev - er west - ward, To the si - lent land of dark - ness, Drift the souls of the de - part - ed To the king - dom of the West Wind.
f
mp
mf
Who knows his path - way ? His lodge of eve - ning ? All the old men have not seen it. All the wise men know noth - ing of it.
Who knows their path - way ? Their lodge of eve - ning ? All the old men have not seen it. All the wise men know noth - ing of it.
p

The Flag

Lucy K. Milburn

Swedish Folk Tune

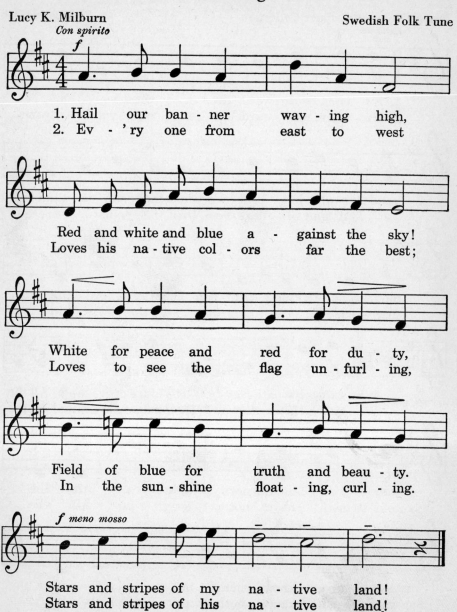

1. Hail our ban - ner wav - ing high,
2. Ev - 'ry one from east to west

Red and white and blue a - gainst the sky!
Loves his na - tive col - ors far the best;

White for peace and red for du - ty,
Loves to see the flag un - furl - ing,

Field of blue for truth and beau - ty.
In the sun - shine float - ing, curl - ing.

Stars and stripes of my na - tive land!
Stars and stripes of his na - tive land!

The Visitor

Mabel Livingstone

Mana-Zucca

Dolce cantabile
mp
1. I saw a lit - tle rob - in,
2. But though I tip - toed soft - ly
A - hop - ping on the gate. · ·
And spoke so sweet and low, · ·
I said, " O, Mis - ter Rob - in, won't you come in -
The rob - in on - ly said, " Cheer-up ! I real - ly
side · and wait ? · · You may sing a - mong my
have · to go,' · · For my ba - by birds are
flow - ers, · · You may swing be - neath my trees. ·
hun - gry ; · · It is time for us · to sup ; ·
mf
O Mis - ter Rob - in, do come in and vis - it,
But I will come an - oth - er day. Cheer - up ! cheer-

won't you, please?" up! cheer-up! Cheer-up! cheer-up! cheer-up!"

Summertime

Mabel Livingstone | ROTE | Victor Young

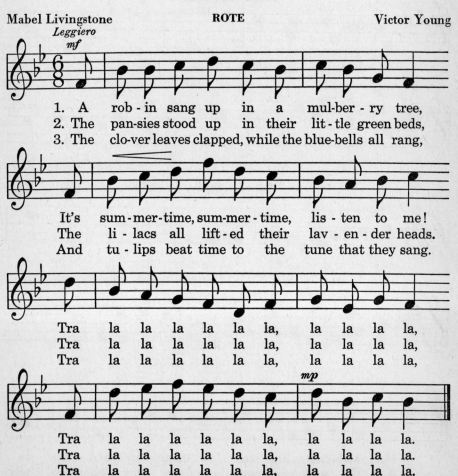

1. A rob - in sang up in a mul-ber - ry tree,
2. The pan-sies stood up in their lit - tle green beds,
3. The clo-ver leaves clapped, while the blue-bells all rang,

It's sum - mer - time, sum-mer - time, lis - ten to me!
The li - lacs all lift - ed their lav - en - der heads.
And tu - lips beat time to the tune that they sang.

Tra la la la la la la, la la la la,
Tra la la la la la la, la la la la,
Tra la la la la la la, la la la la,

Tra la la la la la la, la la la la.
Tra la la la la la la, la la la la.
Tra la la la la la la, la la la la.

The Guardians

Margaret Widdemer — Robert Schumann

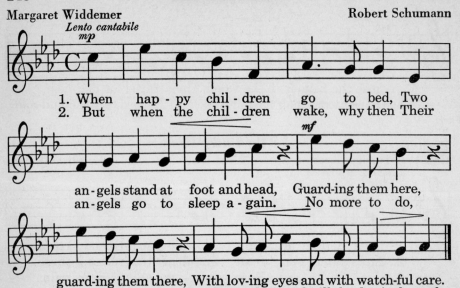

1. When hap - py chil - dren go to bed, Two
2. But when the chil - dren wake, why then Their

an - gels stand at foot and head, Guard-ing them here,
an - gels go to sleep a - gain. No more to do,

guard-ing them there, With lov-ing eyes and with watch-ful care.
no more to do; God keeps the watch till the day is through.

Silver Rain

Frances Ford — Newton Swift

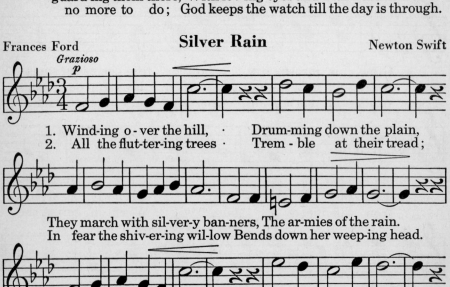

1. Wind-ing o - ver the hill, · Drum-ming down the plain,
2. All the flut-ter-ing trees · Trem - ble at their tread;

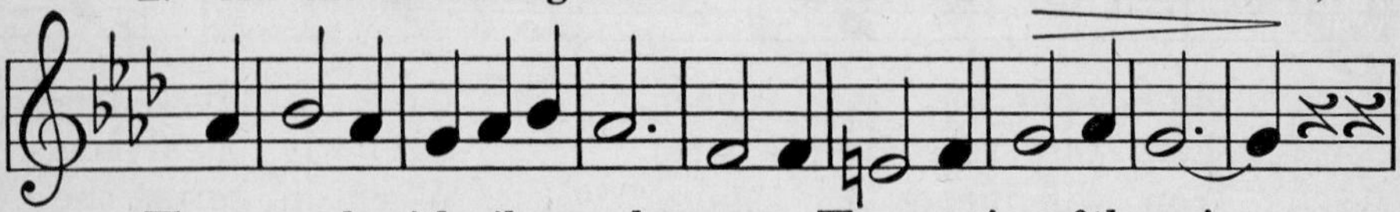

They march with sil-ver-y ban-ners, The ar-mies of the rain.
In fear the shiv-er-ing wil-low Bends down her weep-ing head.

Each with flick-er-ing lance, Each with shin-ing spear,
Un - der wa-ter - y boughs Press the ar - mies bold;

A-cross the field or in the wood, They trav-el far and near.
They nev-er loose their flash-ing spears Till woods are wet and cold.

Little Lady Rose

English version by
Christine Turner Curtis

Polish Folk Song

Andante espressivo

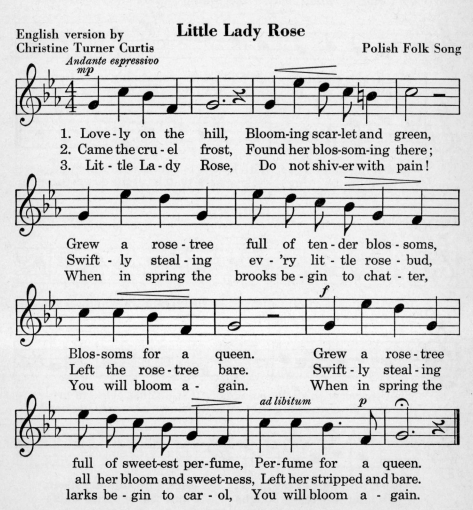

1. Love-ly on the hill, Bloom-ing scar-let and green,
2. Came the cru-el frost, Found her blos-som-ing there;
3. Lit-tle La-dy Rose, Do not shiv-er with pain!

Grew a rose-tree full of ten-der blos-soms,
Swift-ly steal-ing ev-'ry lit-tle rose-bud,
When in spring the brooks be-gin to chat-ter,

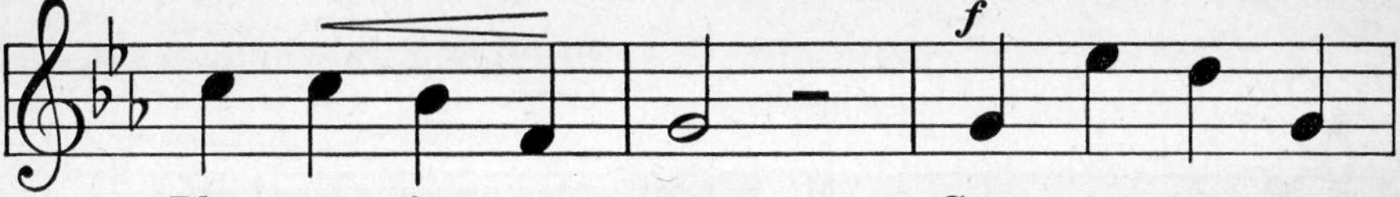

Blos-soms for a queen. Grew a rose-tree
Left the rose-tree bare. Swift-ly steal-ing
You will bloom a-gain. When in spring the

full of sweet-est per-fume, Per-fume for a queen.
all her bloom and sweet-ness, Left her stripped and bare.
larks be-gin to car-ol, You will bloom a-gain.

Sunday Morning

English version by
Marchette Gaylord Chute

German Folk Song

Giocoso
mf
1. I wear a rib - bon on my hair,
2. A - cross the field I hear their sound,
My best of ev - 'ry - thing; And through the fields of
The church bells soft and slow. From ev - 'ry vil - lage
dai-sies fair I hur - ry down, when the church bells ring.
all a-round, The peo - ple come to the church be - low.

Sunset

Edith Robbins

Helen Sewall Leavitt

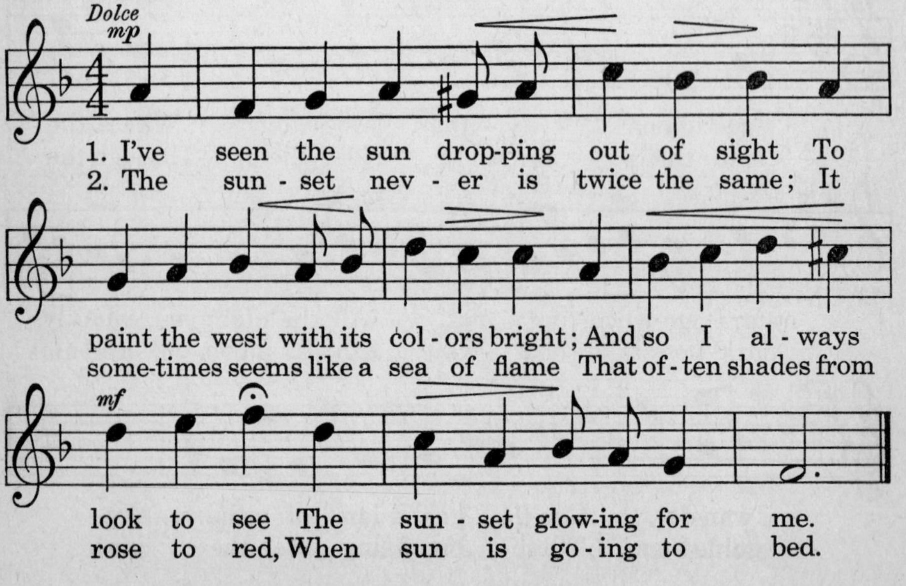
Dolce
mp
1. I've seen the sun drop-ping out of sight To
2. The sun - set nev - er is twice the same; It
paint the west with its col - ors bright; And so I al - ways
some-times seems like a sea of flame That of - ten shades from
mf
look to see The sun - set glow-ing for me.
rose to red, When sun is go - ing to bed.

The Moon

Rose Fyleman | German Folk Tune

Sostenuto
p
1. Love-ly moon, you sail so · light-ly O'er the
2. Far be - neath you lies the · o - cean, Where the
qui - et heav'n-ly · sea, Where you shine so soft and
waves for - ev - er - more Roll with strange and rest-less
bright-ly O-ver wood and hill and lea. Through the
mo-tion, To and fro from shore to shore. Ships that
mf
re - gions ly - ing yon - der, Where the
ride them, brave - ly ride them, Through the
stars go wheel-ing by, · All the night you calm-ly ·
dark-ness take their way. Kind-ly moon, oh, lead and
wan-der, Gen-tle guard-ian of · the · sky.
guide them, Till the break-ing of · the · day!

The Hardy Northman

Translated by
Cecil Cowdrey

Norwegian Folk Song

Con brio
mf
1. Yo - ho! We sing a he - ro bold.
2. With shin - ing hel - met, might - y spear,
Sing, sail - or, sing yo - ho!
Sing, sail - or, sing yo - ho!
He roved the seas in days of old.
He stood for right, for free - dom dear.

Sing, sail - or, sing yo - ho!
Sing, sail - or, sing yo - ho!
Hur - rah! We sing his glo - rious name;
With might - y arm his spear he hurled;
The land and sea be - held his fame. Sing, sail - or, sing!
He saw his flag in peace un-furled. Sing, sail - or, sing!
f
sing, sail - or, sing! Sing, sail - or, sing yo - ho, ho!
sing, sail - or, sing! Sing, sail - or, sing yo - ho, ho!
Sing, sail - or, sing! sing, sail - or, sing!
Sing, sail - or, sing! sing, sail - or, sing!
1
2
Sing, sail-or, sing yo - ho! Sing, sail-or, sing yo - ho, ho!

Village Talk

English version by
Christine Turner Curtis

Polish Folk Song

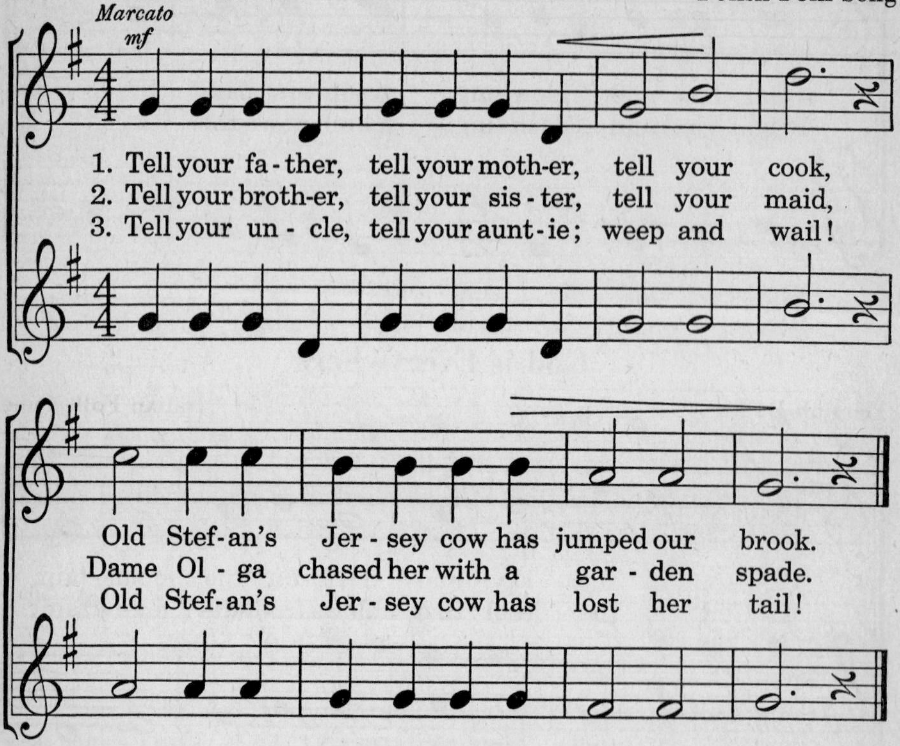
Marcato
mf
1. Tell your fa - ther, tell your moth-er, tell your cook,
2. Tell your broth-er, tell your sis - ter, tell your maid,
3. Tell your un - cle, tell your aunt - ie; weep and wail!
Old Stef - an's Jer - sey cow has jumped our brook.
Dame Ol - ga chased her with a gar - den spade.
Old Stef - an's Jer - sey cow has lost her tail!

The Troopers

Frances Ford

Austrian Folk Tune

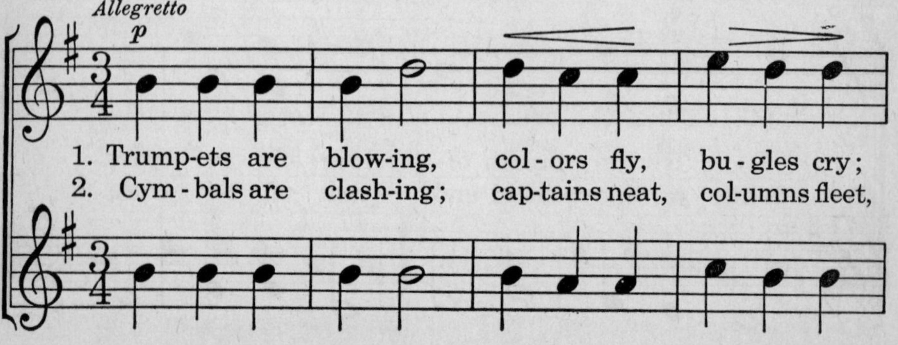
Allegretto
p
1. Trump-ets are blow-ing, col - ors fly, bu - gles cry;
2. Cym - bals are clash-ing; cap-tains neat, col-umns fleet,

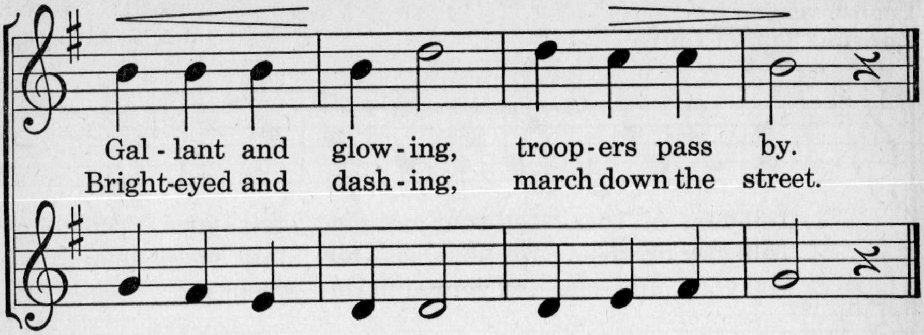
Gal - lant and glow - ing, troop - ers pass by.
Bright-eyed and dash - ing, march down the street.

God is Everywhere

Hannah Bailey

Italian Folk Tune

Legato
mp
1. Deep in the sky, and dark on the moun - tain,
2. God is the cool that blows from the foun - tain;

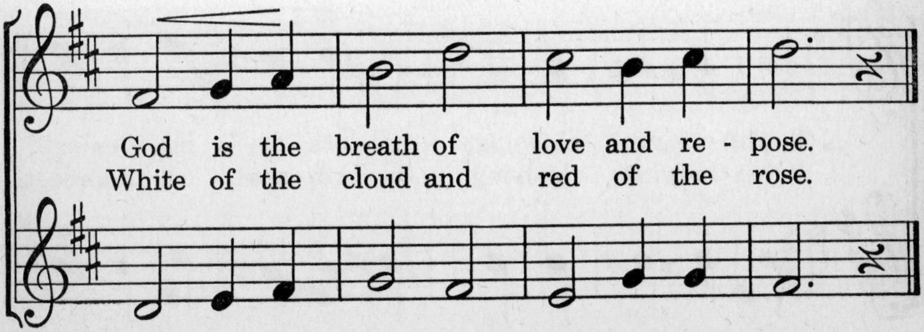
God is the breath of love and re - pose.
White of the cloud and red of the rose.

Gardening

Lois Lenski

Johann H. G. Nägeli

Andantino
mf

1. I have a gar-den, I have a hoe;
2. Warm is the sun-shine, Gen-tle the rain;
3. Mar-i-golds yel-low, Zin-ni-as red,

Slow-ly I'm plant-ing The seeds in a row.
Weeds grow so quick-ly, I hoe them a-gain.
Gay-ly are bloom-ing In my gar-den bed.

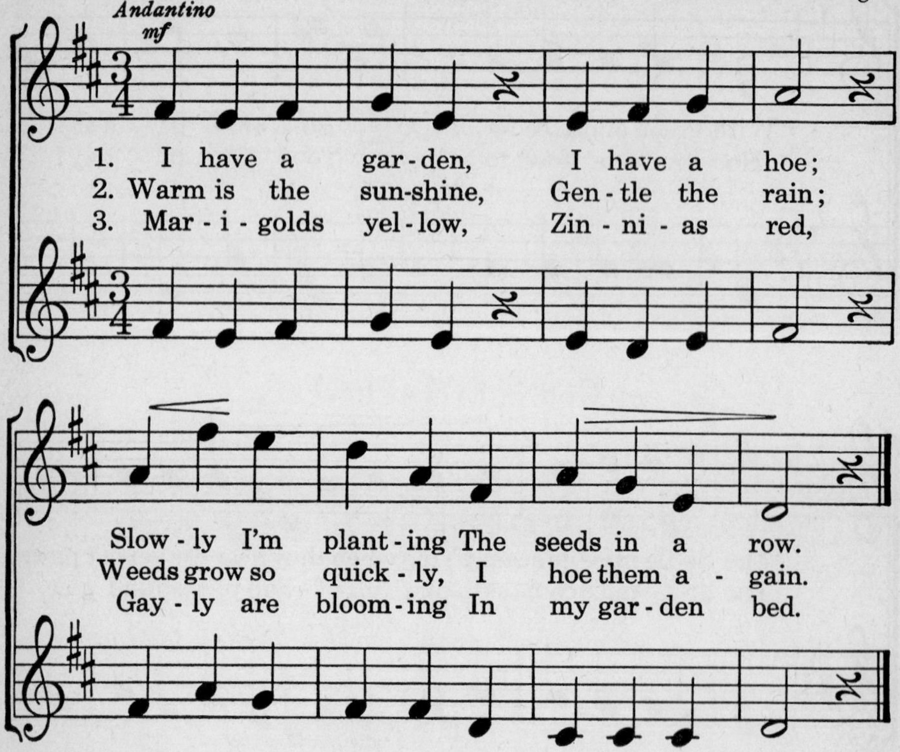

The Mouser

Translated by
Frances Ford

Austrian Folk Song

Giocoso
mf f p

1. The cat comes creep-ing by; Take care, take care!
2. The cat has gone a-way; A-way, a-way!

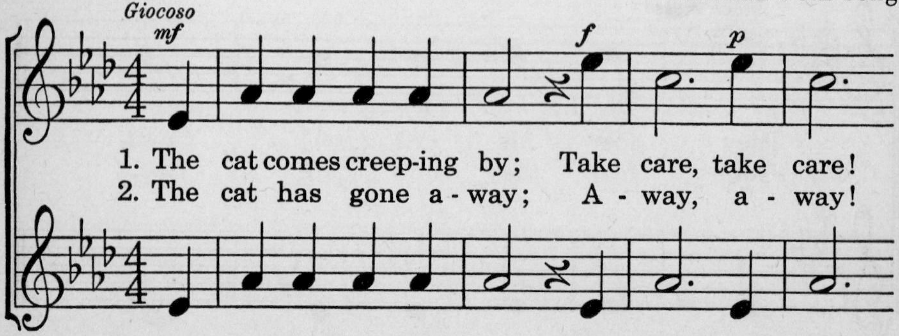

f
p
With green and greed-y eye; Be - ware, be - ware!
No mous - ie food to - day; To - day, to - day!
The lit-tle mice go scam-p'ring when they hear his vel-vet paws.
The lit-tle mice come skip-ping full of hap-pi-ness and glee.
meno mosso
They fear his cru - el claws.
From fear they now are free.

The Harp of the Winds

Marjorie Knapp — Theo Halle

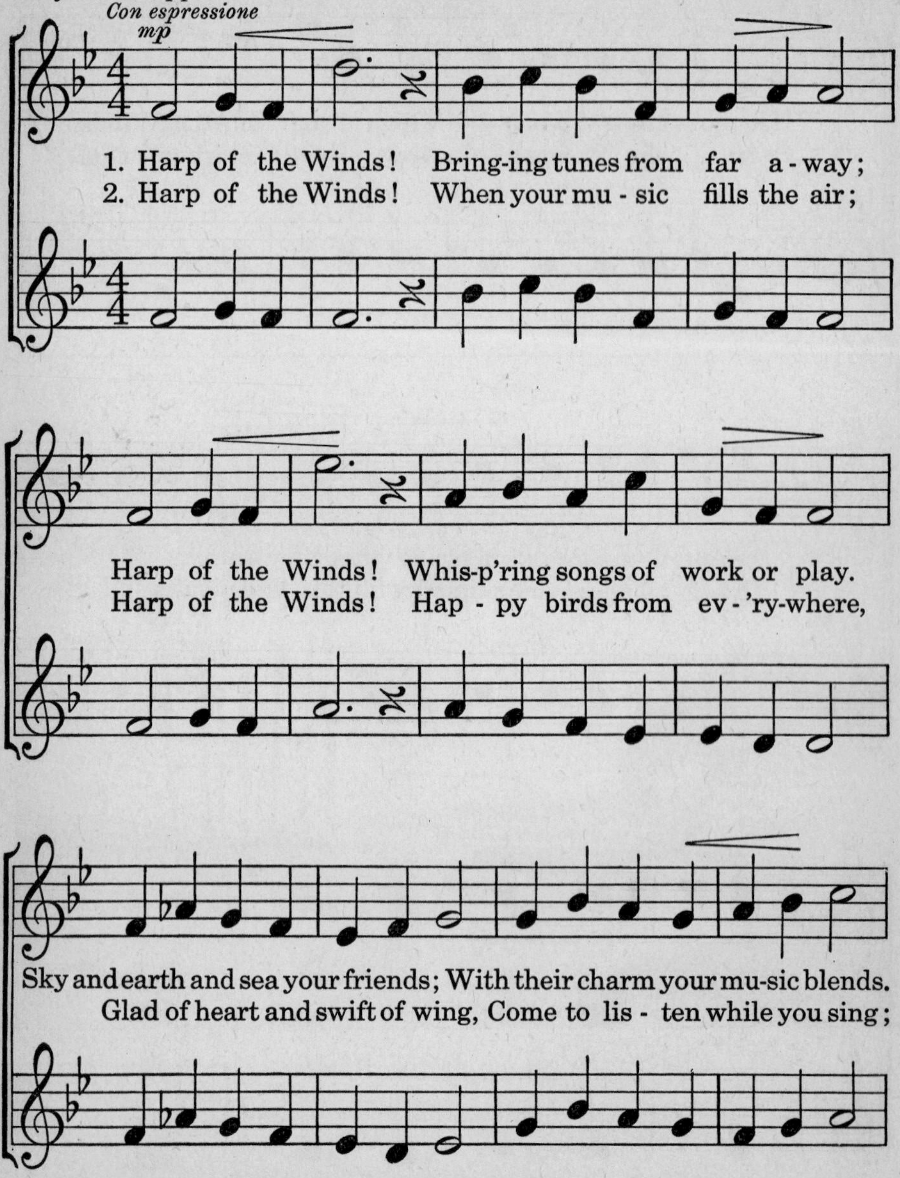
Con espressione
mp
1. Harp of the Winds! Bring-ing tunes from far a-way;
2. Harp of the Winds! When your mu-sic fills the air;
Harp of the Winds! Whis-p'ring songs of work or play.
Harp of the Winds! Hap-py birds from ev-'ry-where,
Sky and earth and sea your friends; With their charm your mu-sic blends.
Glad of heart and swift of wing, Come to lis-ten while you sing;

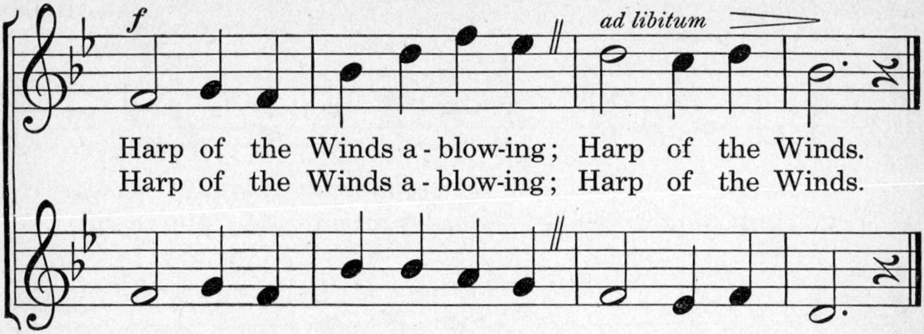
f
ad libitum
Harp of the Winds a - blow-ing; Harp of the Winds.
Harp of the Winds a - blow-ing; Harp of the Winds.

The Art Extension Press, Inc.

The Harp of the Winds

Painted by the American artist HOMER D. MARTIN

Moon of Silver White

Christine Turner Curtis

Franz Schubert

Adagio cantabile
p
1. "Tell me, tell me, moon of sil - ver white,
2. "Tell me, tell me, moon of sil - ver white,
Through my cham - ber win - dow peep - ing,
Through my cham - ber win - dow beam - ing,
Why you wan - der in the lone - ly night,
Why you wake me in the lone - ly night,
When all folk be - low are sleep - ing?"
With your glanc - es soft - ly stream - ing?"
mf
"When the twi - light fades from the skies,
"When the shad - ows dark - en and fall,
When the lil - ies close their cream - y eyes,
When the night en - folds the ma - ples tall;

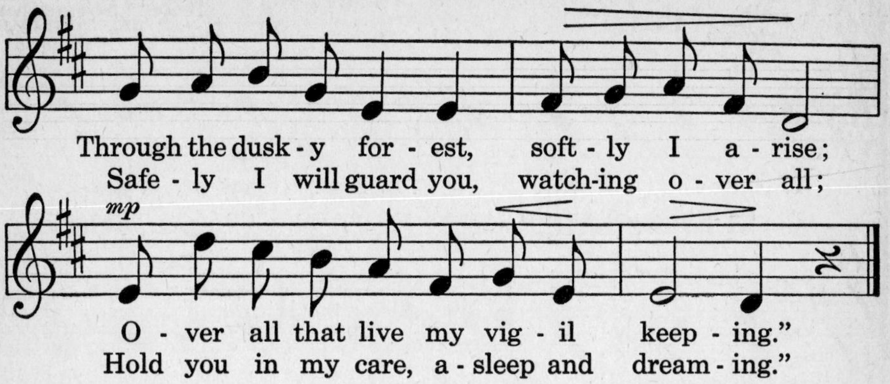
Through the dusk - y for - est, soft - ly I a - rise;
Safe - ly I will guard you, watch-ing o - ver all;
mp
O - ver all that live my vig - il keep - ing."
Hold you in my care, a - sleep and dream - ing."

Magic

Frances Ford

Czech Folk Tune

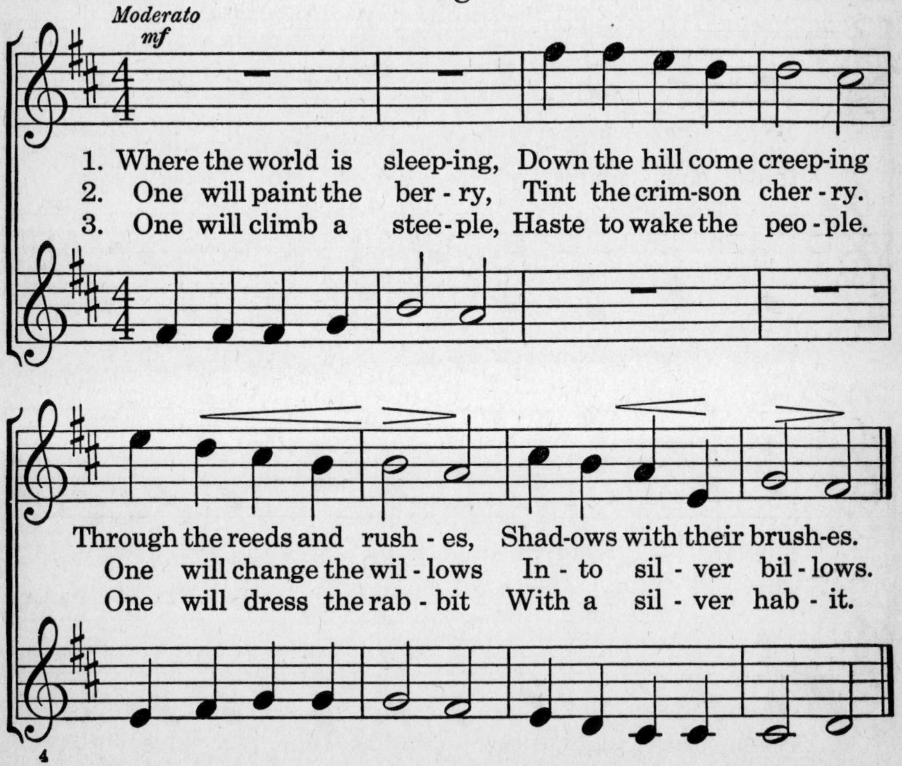
Moderato
mf
1. Where the world is sleep-ing, Down the hill come creep-ing
2. One will paint the ber - ry, Tint the crim-son cher - ry.
3. One will climb a stee - ple, Haste to wake the peo - ple.
Through the reeds and rush - es, Shad-ows with their brush-es.
One will change the wil - lows In - to sil - ver bil - lows.
One will dress the rab - bit With a sil - ver hab - it.

Gratitude

M. A. L. Lane

Robert Schumann

Sostenuto
mp
1. Soon the sun will go to rest. Slow - ly, sure - ly
2. Fa - ther, we would give Thee praise For the bless-ings
it is sink - ing, Drop - ping down be -
that sur - round us. For the joys that
rallentando
low the west: 'Tis the hour we love the best.
fill our days Grate - ful thanks to Thee we raise.

The May Queen

Marchette Gaylord Chute | Bohemian Folk Tune

Semplice
mf
1. Where blue vio - lets may be seen,
2. We put flow - ers in her hair;
Where the grass grows soft and green, There we crowned her
We hung gar - lands ev - 'ry-where; Then we danced a -
f
for our queen: Charm - ing queen of May - time.
bout her there, All our hap - py play - time.

The Bold Hunter

English version by
Cecil Cowdrey

Austrian Folk Song

Con spirito
f

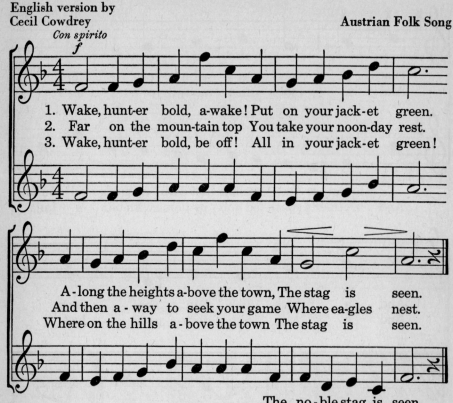

1. Wake, hunt-er bold, a-wake! Put on your jack-et green.
2. Far on the moun-tain top You take your noon-day rest.
3. Wake, hunt-er bold, be off! All in your jack-et green!

A-long the heights a-bove the town, The stag is seen.
And then a-way to seek your game Where ea-gles nest.
Where on the hills a-bove the town The stag is seen.

The no-ble stag is seen.
Where ea-gles build their nest.
The no-ble stag is seen.

The Attic

G. A. Grant-Schaefer

ROTE

G. A. Grant-Schaefer

Vivace
mf

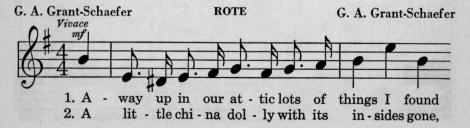

1. A - way up in our at - tic lots of things I found
2. A lit - tle chi - na dol - ly with its in - sides gone,

That I nev - er saw be - fore:
And a sol - dier made of lead;
I found a fad - ed bon - net with a fringe all round,
And broth-er's speck-led hob - by-horse with-out a tail,
And a blue dish on the floor.
And a tall, old, four - post bed.

Wild Winds

Philip Muzzy

Yugoslavian Folk Tune

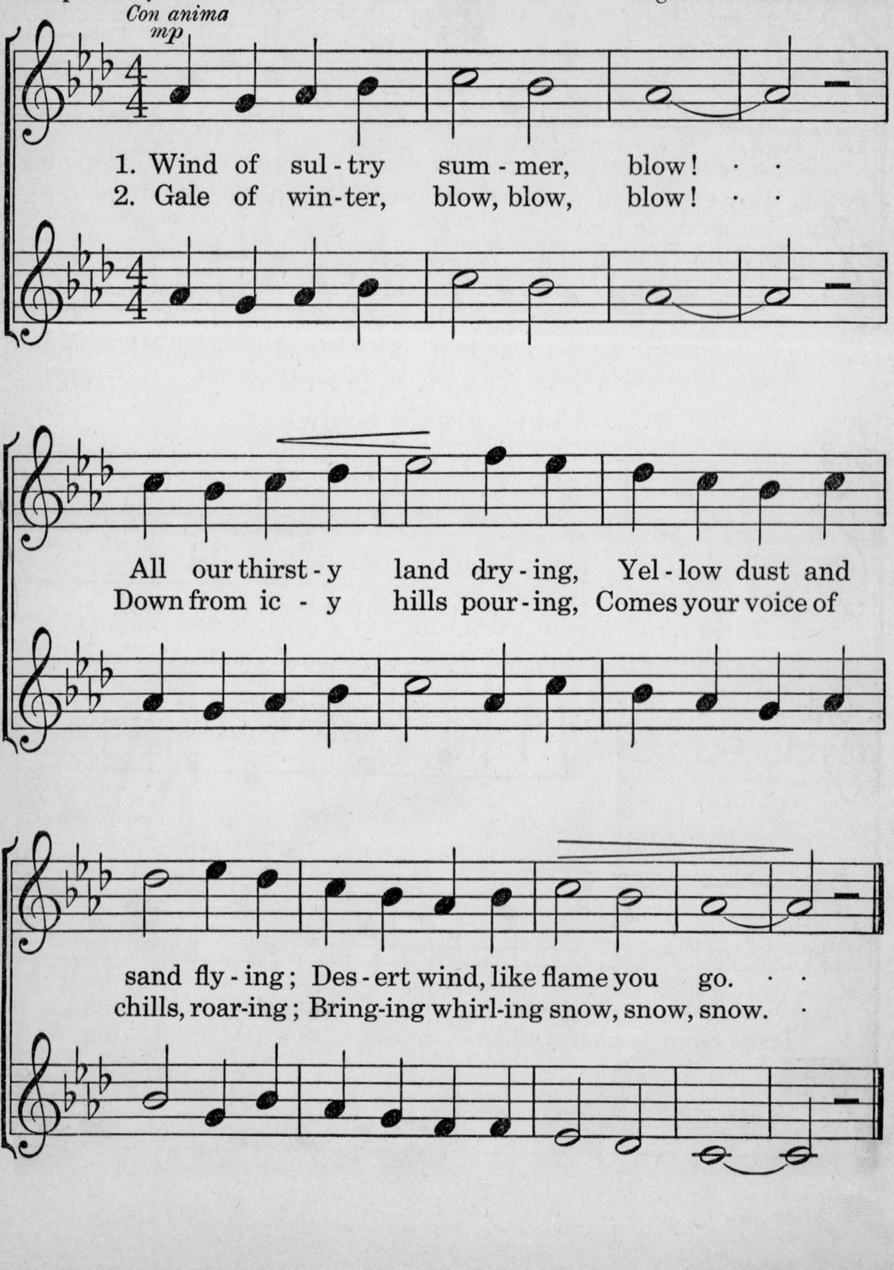
Con anima
mp
1. Wind of sul-try sum-mer, blow!
2. Gale of win-ter, blow, blow, blow!
All our thirst-y land dry-ing, Yel-low dust and
Down from ic-y hills pour-ing, Comes your voice of
sand fly-ing; Des-ert wind, like flame you go.
chills, roar-ing; Bring-ing whirl-ing snow, snow, snow.

Shopping

Anne White | Russian Folk Melody

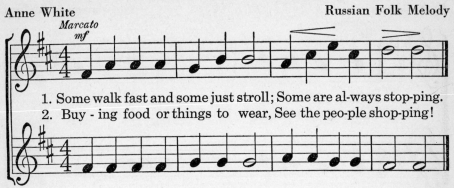

1. Some walk fast and some just stroll; Some are al-ways stop-ping.
2. Buy - ing food or things to wear, See the peo-ple shop-ping!

Where Music Grows

Carol Fuller | Ludwig van Beethoven

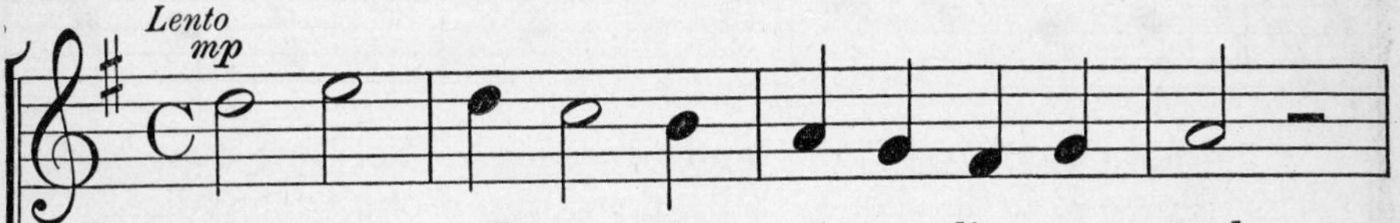

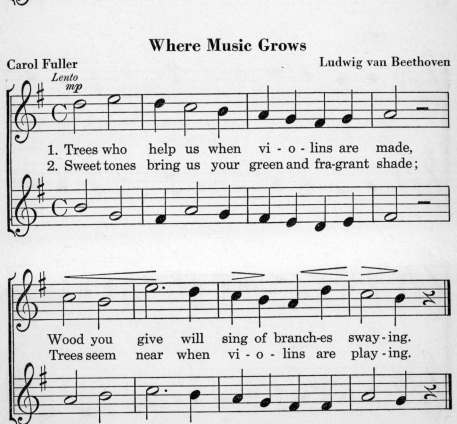

1. Trees who help us when vi - o - lins are made,
2. Sweet tones bring us your green and fra-grant shade;

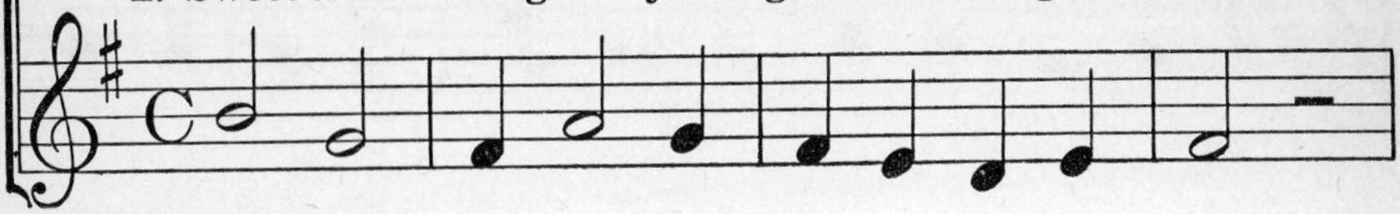

Wood you give will sing of branch-es sway - ing.
Trees seem near when vi - o - lins are play - ing.

The Water Wheel

M. A. L. Lane

Viennese Melody

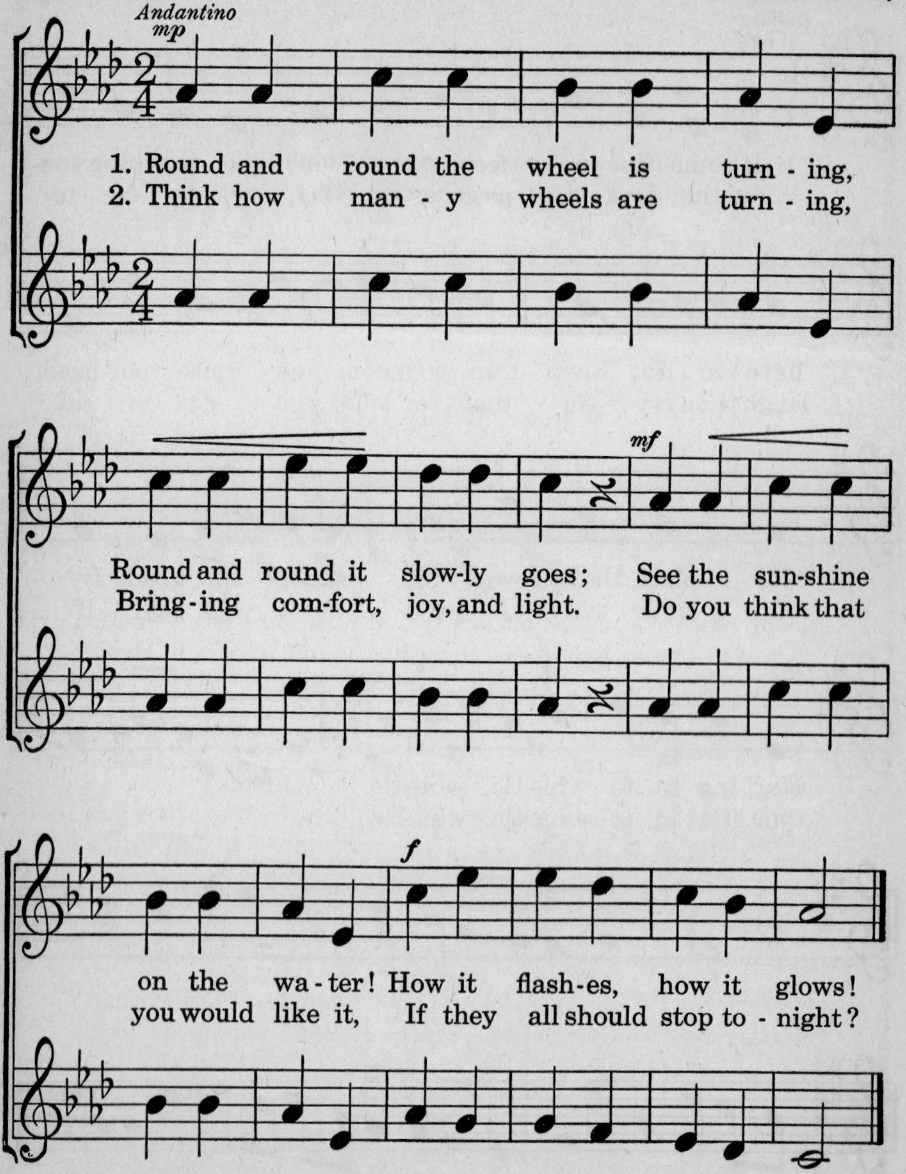
Andantino
mp
1. Round and round the wheel is turn - ing,
2. Think how man - y wheels are turn - ing,
Round and round it slow-ly goes; See the sun-shine
Bring-ing com-fort, joy, and light. Do you think that
mf
on the wa-ter! How it flash-es, how it glows!
you would like it, If they all should stop to - night?
f

Whistle

Victor Young — Victor Young

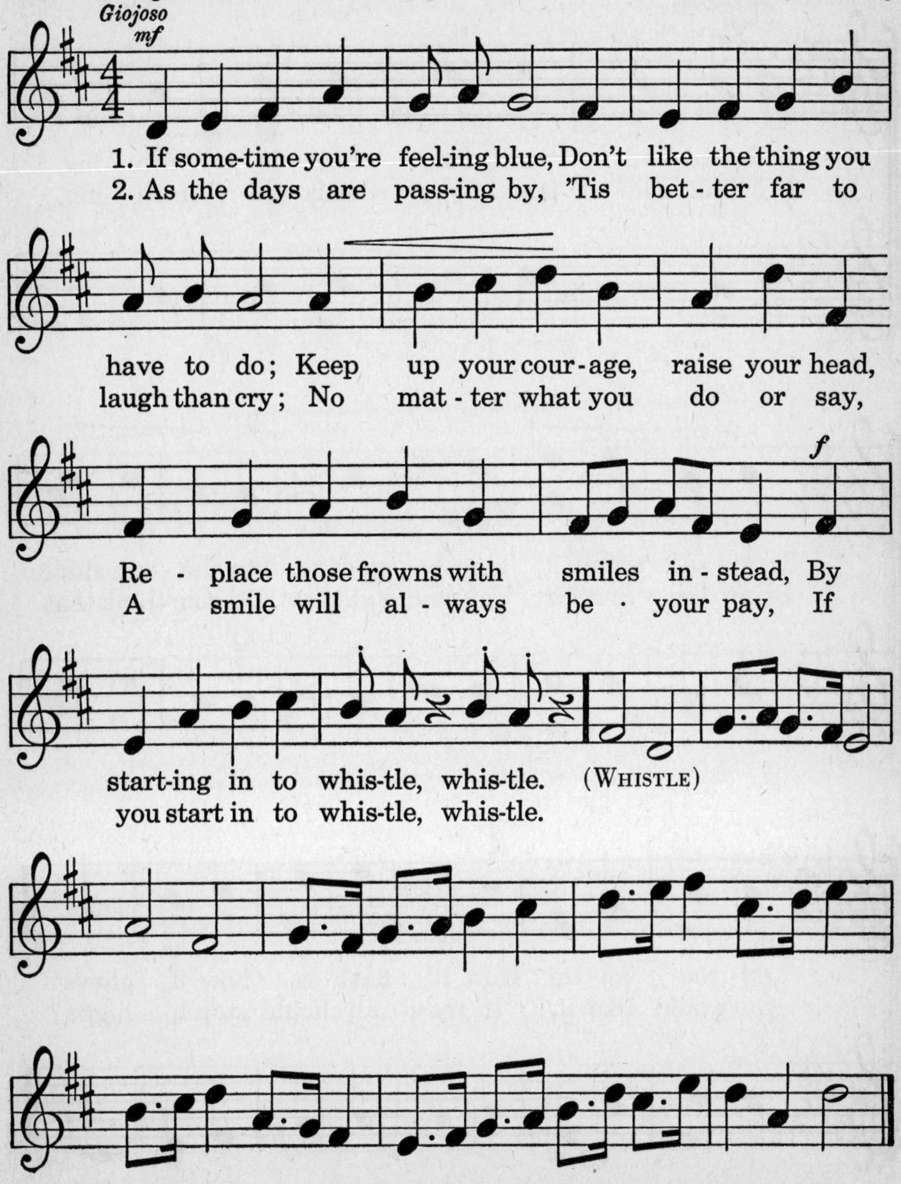
Giojoso
mf
1. If some-time you're feel-ing blue, Don't like the thing you
2. As the days are pass-ing by, 'Tis bet - ter far to
have to do; Keep up your cour - age, raise your head,
laugh than cry; No mat - ter what you do or say,
f
Re - place those frowns with smiles in - stead, By
A smile will al - ways be · your pay, If
start-ing in to whis-tle, whis-tle. (WHISTLE)
you start in to whis-tle, whis-tle.

On Memorial Day

Carol Fuller | E. Meyer-Helmund

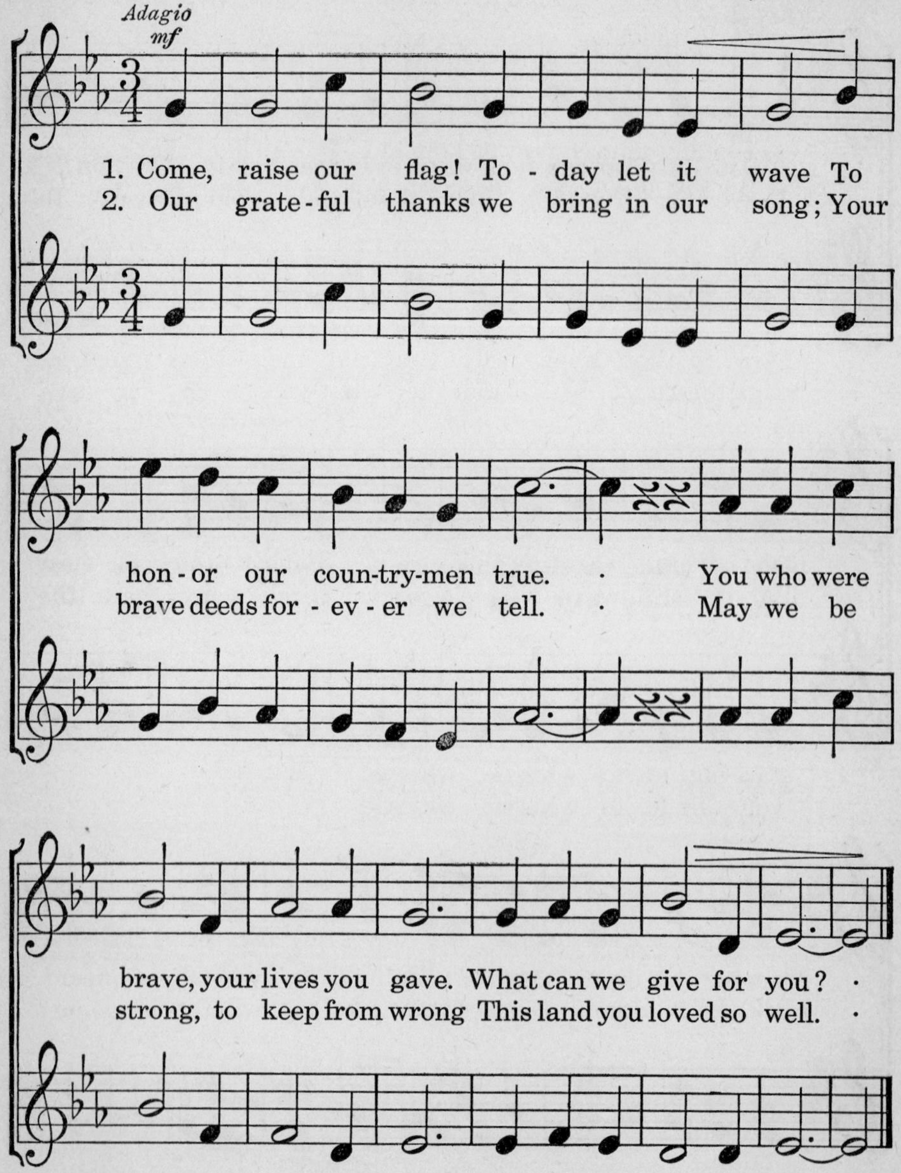
Adagio
mf
1. Come, raise our flag! To - day let it wave To
2. Our grate - ful thanks we bring in our song; Your
hon - or our coun-try-men true. You who were
brave deeds for - ev - er we tell. May we be
brave, your lives you gave. What can we give for you?
strong, to keep from wrong This land you loved so well.

On the Baltic

English version by
Christine Turner Curtis

Estonian Folk Song

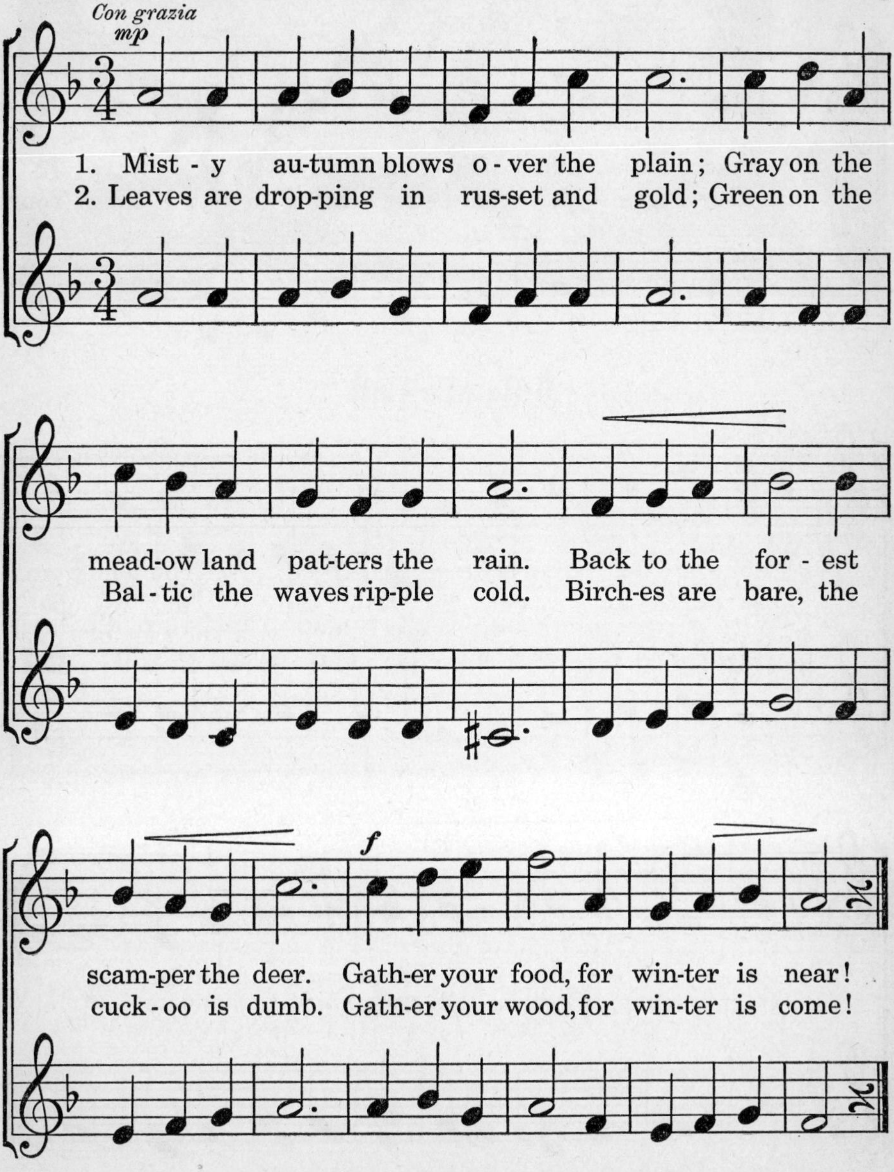
Con grazia
mp
1. Mist - y au-tumn blows o - ver the plain; Gray on the
2. Leaves are drop-ping in rus-set and gold; Green on the
mead-ow land pat-ters the rain. Back to the for - est
Bal - tic the waves rip-ple cold. Birch-es are bare, the
f
scam-per the deer. Gath-er your food, for win-ter is near!
cuck - oo is dumb. Gath-er your wood, for win-ter is come!

Roland's Call

Translated by
Philip Muzzy

French-Canadian Folk Song

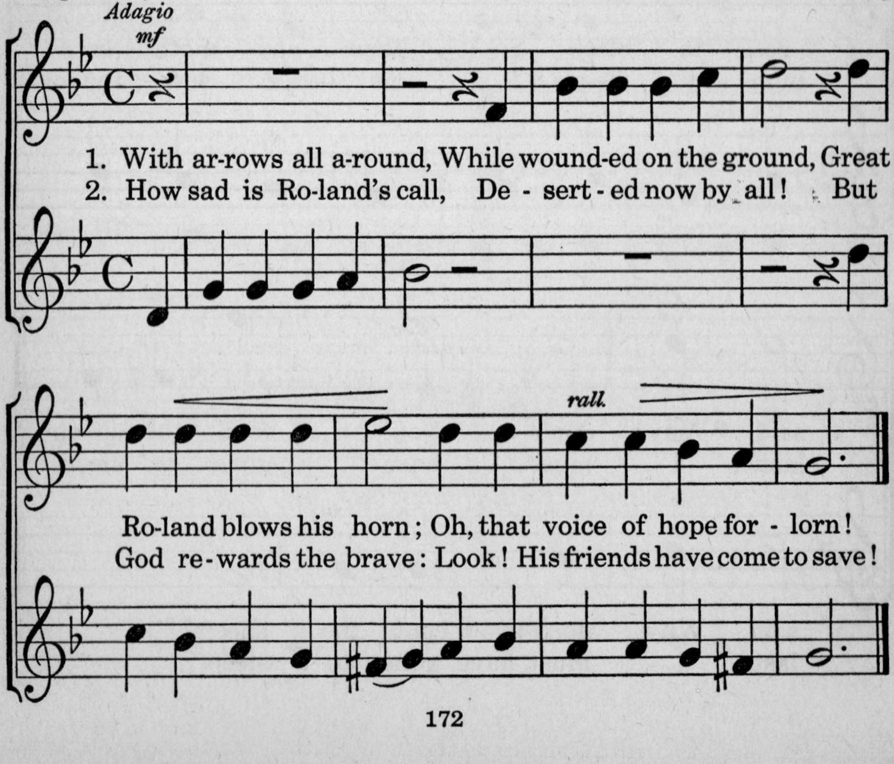
Adagio
mf
1. With ar-rows all a-round, While wound-ed on the ground, Great
2. How sad is Ro-land's call, De - sert - ed now by all! But
rall.
Ro-land blows his horn; Oh, that voice of hope for - lorn!
God re-wards the brave: Look! His friends have come to save!

Counting Sheep

Elizabeth C. Taylor

Swedish Folk Tune

Legato
mf
1. One night I went to bed, And found I could not
2. I count-ed ver - y fast; But soon there were so
go to sleep; So then my moth - er
man - y sheep, I nev - er saw the
f
said, "Why don't you count the sheep?"
last. I must have gone to sleep.
said, "Why don't you count the sheep?"
last. I must have gone to sleep.

A Summer Song

Kathleen Malone

Jacques Offenbach

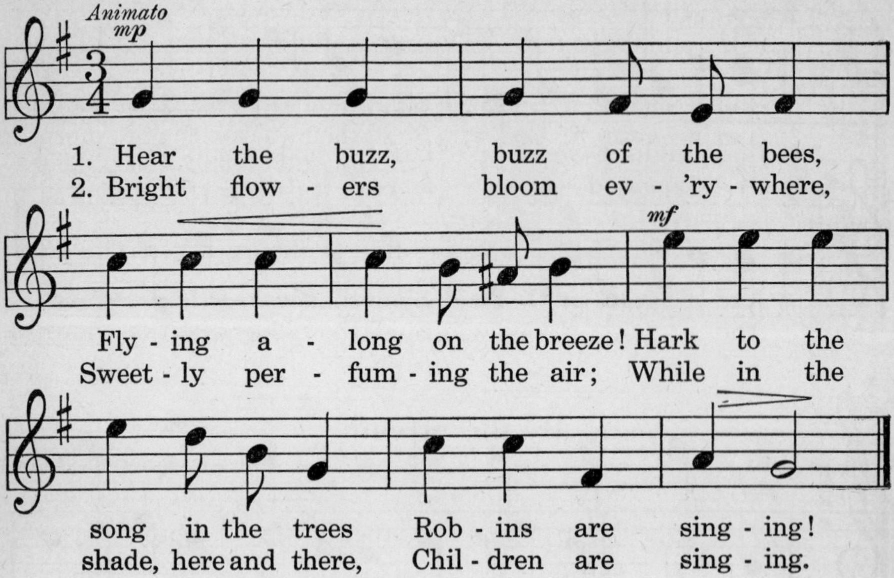
Animato
mp
1. Hear the buzz, buzz of the bees,
2. Bright flow - ers bloom ev - 'ry - where,
Fly - ing a - long on the breeze! Hark to the
Sweet - ly per - fum - ing the air; While in the
mf
song in the trees Rob - ins are sing - ing!
shade, here and there, Chil - dren are sing - ing.

Slumber Song

ROTE

Karl Simrock
Translated

Johannes Brahms

Tranquillamente
p
1. Lull - a - by and good-night! To cheeks ros - y bright,
2. Lull - a - by and good-night! Till glad morn-ing light,
To · fin-gers safe hid 'Neath cov - er - let white;
While fair-est of · forms In · dreams fill the sight;

And a - gain, if God will, Shalt thou wake with the morn,
And a - gain, if God will, Shalt thou wake with the morn,
pp
rall.
And a - gain, if God will, Shalt thou wake with the morn.
And a - gain, if God will, Shalt thou wake with the morn.

By the Stream

Frances Ford — Yugoslavian Folk Tune

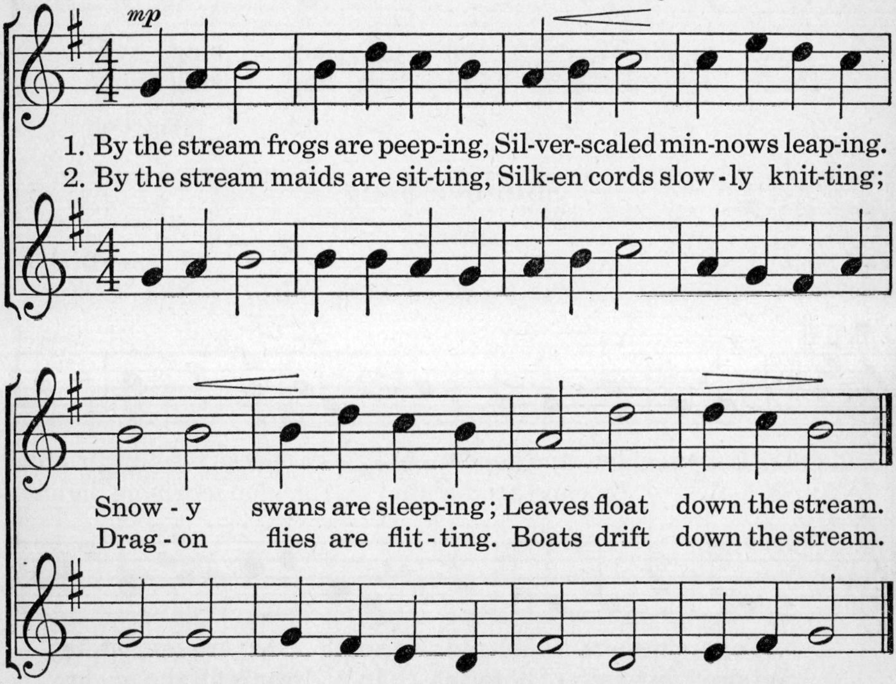
mp
1. By the stream frogs are peep-ing, Sil-ver-scaled min-nows leap-ing.
2. By the stream maids are sit-ting, Silk-en cords slow - ly knit-ting;
Snow - y swans are sleep-ing; Leaves float down the stream.
Drag - on flies are flit - ting. Boats drift down the stream.

Bell Song

Eleanor Farjeon | Polish Folk Tune

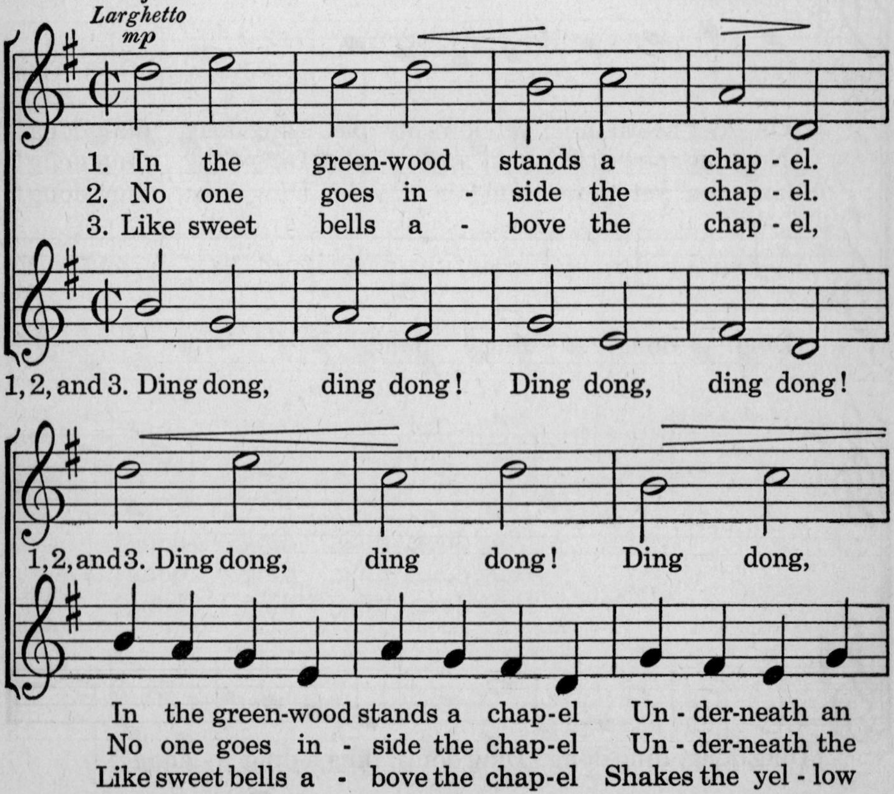
Larghetto
mp
1. In the green-wood stands a chap - el.
2. No one goes in - side the chap - el.
3. Like sweet bells a - bove the chap - el,
1, 2, and 3. Ding dong, ding dong! Ding dong, ding dong!
1, 2, and 3. Ding dong, ding dong! Ding dong,
In the green-wood stands a chap-el Un - der-neath an
No one goes in - side the chap-el Un - der-neath the
Like sweet bells a - bove the chap-el Shakes the yel - low

mf
ding dong! In the green-wood stands a chap-el,
ding dong! No one goes in - side the chap-el,
ding dong! Like sweet bells a - bove the chap-el
1,2,and 3. ap-ple tree, Ding dong, ding dong,
molto crescendo
f
Un - der-neath a yel-low ap - ple. Ding dong, ding dong!
No one comes to shake an ap - ple. Ding dong, ding dong!
Shakes the yel - low, mel-low ap - ple. Ding dong, ding dong!
Ding dong, ding dong.
diminuendo
mp
Ding dong, ding, ding, dong!
Ding dong, ding, ding, dong!
Ding dong, ding, ding, dong!
Ding dong, ding dong! Ding dong! ding-a-ding a - dong!

The Warning

Clara Louise Kessler — Hungarian Folk Tune

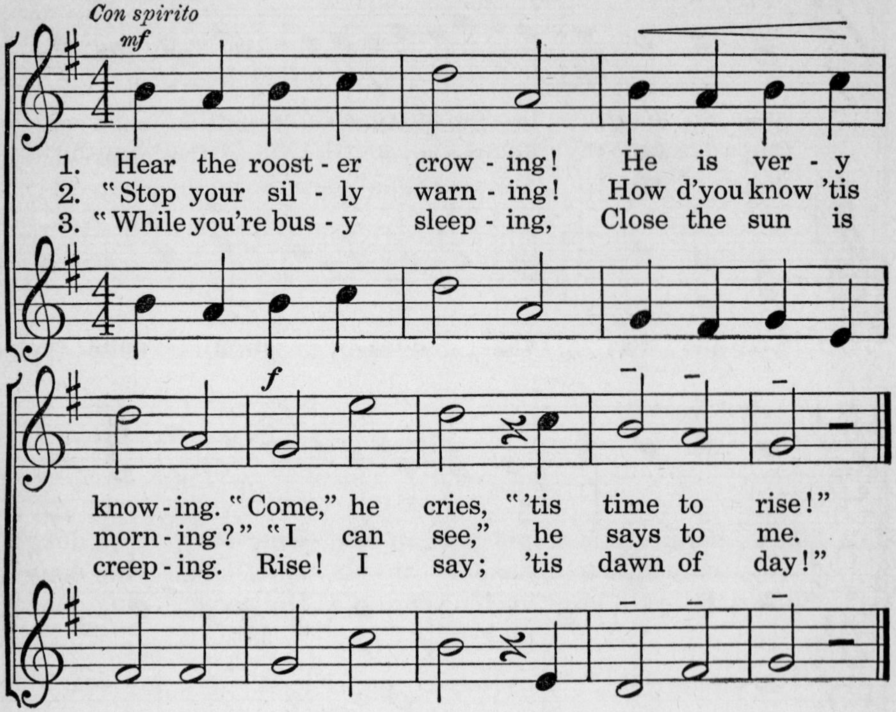
Con spirito
mf
1. Hear the roost - er crow - ing! He is ver - y
2. "Stop your sil - ly warn - ing! How d'you know 'tis
3. "While you're bus - y sleep - ing, Close the sun is
f
know - ing. "Come," he cries, "'tis time to rise!"
morn - ing?" "I can see," he says to me.
creep - ing. Rise! I say; 'tis dawn of day!"

Tea Party Talk

D. E. Wheeler — ROTE — Victor Young

Giocoso con espressione
mf
1. "So pleased to meet you, Mis - sis Jones;
2. "Poor Ma - ry Jane has got the croup;
Why how do you do, dear Mis - sis Brown. Oh,
The maids are not what they used to be! I

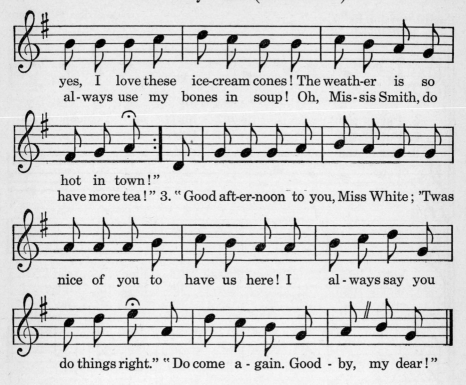

yes, I love these ice-cream cones! The weath-er is so
al-ways use my bones in soup! Oh, Mis-sis Smith, do

hot in town!"
have more tea!" 3. "Good aft-er-noon to you, Miss White; 'Twas

nice of you to have us here! I al-ways say you

do things right." "Do come a-gain. Good-by, my dear!"

Summer Afternoon

Anne White | Hungarian Folk Melody

Andante
mp

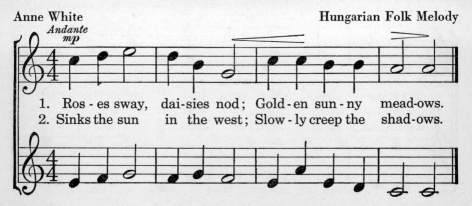

1. Ros-es sway, dai-sies nod; Gold-en sun-ny mead-ows.
2. Sinks the sun in the west; Slow-ly creep the shad-ows.

A Sleepy Song

English version by
Laura E. Richards

Swedish Folk Song

Leggiero
mf
1. Put the lit - tle birds to sleep,
2. Put the ros - y buds to sleep,
3. Put the wea - ry child to sleep,
Hush the lit - tle drow - sy cheep! Drow - sy cheep,
Not a drop of dew to weep. Dew to weep,
Soft - ly, soft - ly croon and creep. Croon and creep,
drow - sy cheep! Moth - er bird is nigh. . .
dew to weep! Moth - er rose is nigh. . .
croon and creep! Moth - er dear is nigh. . .

A Bumblebee

Fanny Giralda Pheatt — Fanny Giralda Pheatt

Leggiero
mp
1. A bus - y lit - tle fel - low Is
2. He must en - joy the hon - ey He
Mis - ter Bum - ble - bee; His suit of black and
sips from ev - 'ry bloom; For all a - round the
mf
yel - low Is as styl - ish as can be.
gar - den I can hear his, "Zoom, zoom, zoom."

America

S. F. Smith

Henry Carey

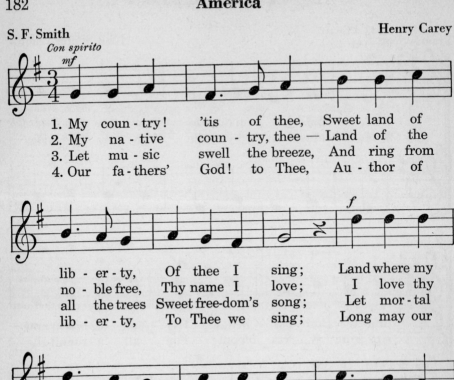

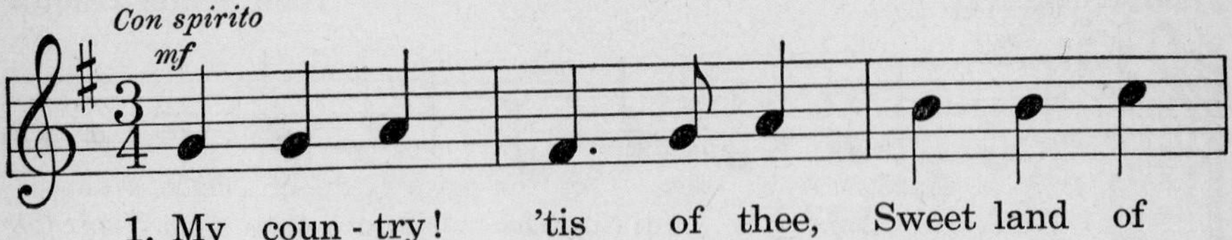

1. My coun - try! 'tis of thee, Sweet land of
2. My na - tive coun - try, thee — Land of the
3. Let mu - sic swell the breeze, And ring from
4. Our fa - thers' God! to Thee, Au - thor of

lib - er - ty, Of thee I sing; Land where my
no - ble free, Thy name I love; I love thy
all the trees Sweet free-dom's song; Let mor - tal
lib - er - ty, To Thee we sing; Long may our

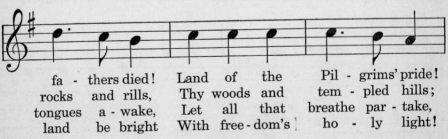

fa - thers died! Land of the Pil - grims' pride!
rocks and rills, Thy woods and tem - pled hills;
tongues a - wake, Let all that breathe par - take,
land be bright With free - dom's ho - ly light!

From ev - 'ry moun - tain side Let free-dom ring!
My heart with rap - ture thrills Like that a - bove.
Let rocks their si - lence break, The sound pro - long.
Pro - tect us by Thy might, Great God, our King!

The Star-Spangled Banner

Francis Scott Key — John Stafford Smith

Con spirito
1. Oh, · say! can you see, · by the dawn's ear - ly light, What so
2. On the shore, dim - ly seen thro' the mists of the deep, Where the
3. Oh, · thus be it ev - er when free - men shall stand Be -
proud - ly we hailed at the twi - light's last gleam - ing, Whose broad
foe's haugh-ty host in dread si - lence re - pos - es, What is
tween their loved homes and the war's des - o - la - tion! Blest with
stripes and bright stars, thro' the per - il - ous fight, O'er the ram-parts we
that which the breeze, o'er the tow - er - ing steep, As it fit - ful - ly
vic - t'ry and peace, may the Heav'n-res-cued land Praise the Pow'r that hath
watch'd were so gal - lant - ly stream-ing? And the rock - ets' red glare,
blows, half con-ceals, half dis - clos - es? Now it catch - es the gleam
made and pre-served us a na - tion! Then con - quer we must,
the bombs burst-ing in air, Gave proof thro' the night that our
of the morn-ing's first beam, In full glo - ry re - flect-ed, now ·
when our cause it is just, And · this be our mot - to: "In · ·
CHORUS
flag was still there. Oh, · say, does that Star-span-gled Ban-ner yet
shines on the stream. 'Tis the Star-span-gled Ban-ner: oh, long may it
God is our trust!" And the Star-span-gled Ban-ner in tri - umph shall
wave · O'er the land · · of the free and the home of the brave!

All Through the Night

Old Welsh | Welsh Folk Song | David Owen

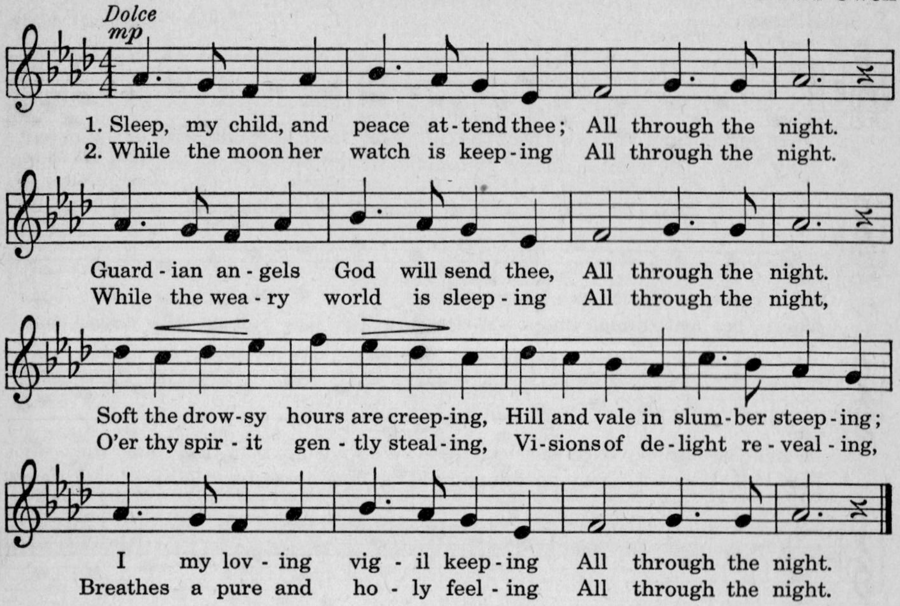
Dolce
mp
1. Sleep, my child, and peace at-tend thee; All through the night.
2. While the moon her watch is keep-ing All through the night.
Guard-ian an-gels God will send thee, All through the night.
While the wea-ry world is sleep-ing All through the night,
Soft the drow-sy hours are creep-ing, Hill and vale in slum-ber steep-ing;
O'er thy spir-it gen-tly steal-ing, Vi-sions of de-light re-veal-ing,
I my lov-ing vig-il keep-ing All through the night.
Breathes a pure and ho-ly feel-ing All through the night.

For the Beauty of the Earth

Folliott S. Pierpont | Arranged from Conrad Kocher

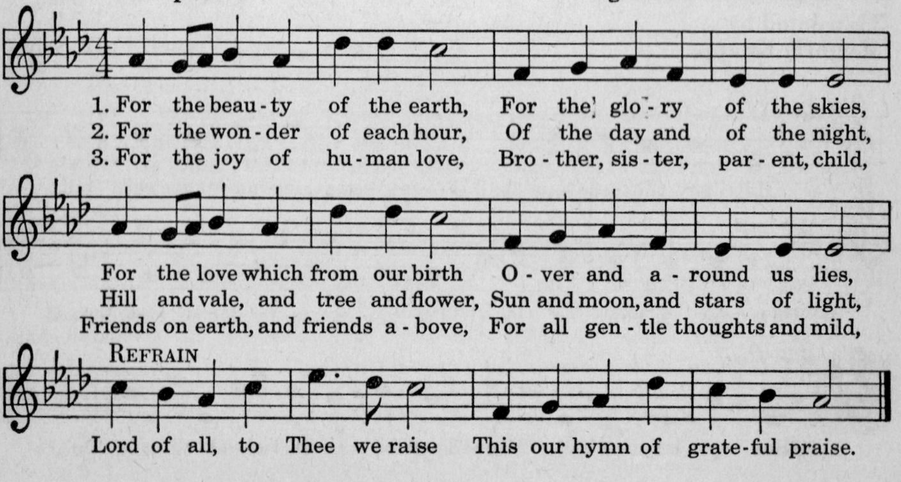
1. For the beau-ty of the earth, For the glo-ry of the skies,
2. For the won-der of each hour, Of the day and of the night,
3. For the joy of hu-man love, Bro-ther, sis-ter, par-ent, child,
For the love which from our birth O-ver and a-round us lies,
Hill and vale, and tree and flower, Sun and moon, and stars of light,
Friends on earth, and friends a-bove, For all gen-tle thoughts and mild,
Refrain
Lord of all, to Thee we raise This our hymn of grate-ful praise.

Play Ball

Morris Carter

English Folk Tune

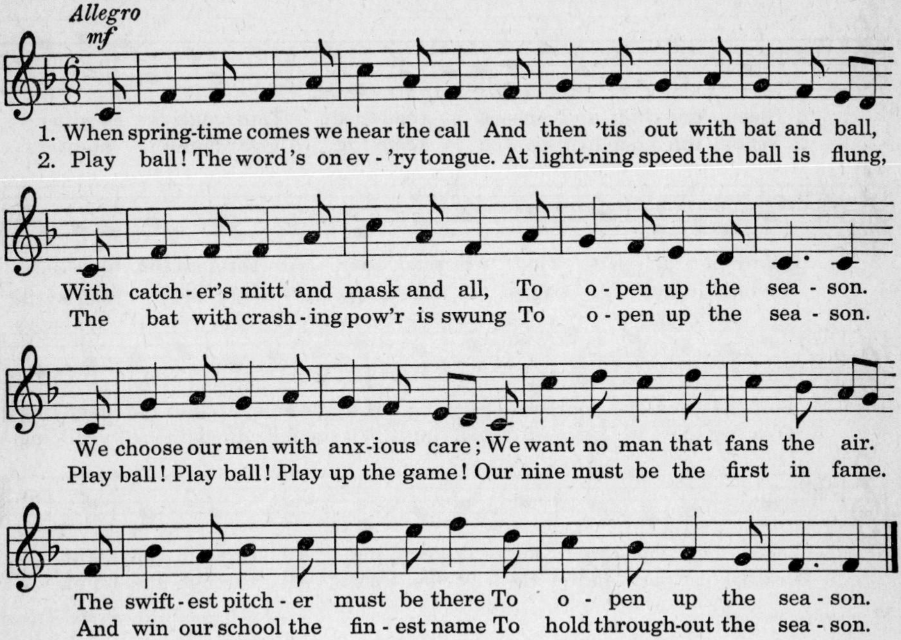
Allegro
mf
1. When spring-time comes we hear the call And then 'tis out with bat and ball,
2. Play ball! The word's on ev - 'ry tongue. At light-ning speed the ball is flung,
With catch - er's mitt and mask and all, To o - pen up the sea - son.
The bat with crash - ing pow'r is swung To o - pen up the sea - son.
We choose our men with anx-ious care; We want no man that fans the air.
Play ball! Play ball! Play up the game! Our nine must be the first in fame.
The swift - est pitch - er must be there To o - pen up the sea - son.
And win our school the fin - est name To hold through-out the sea - son.

Round: The Ball of the Seasons

Translated by
Marjorie Knapp

French Folk Song

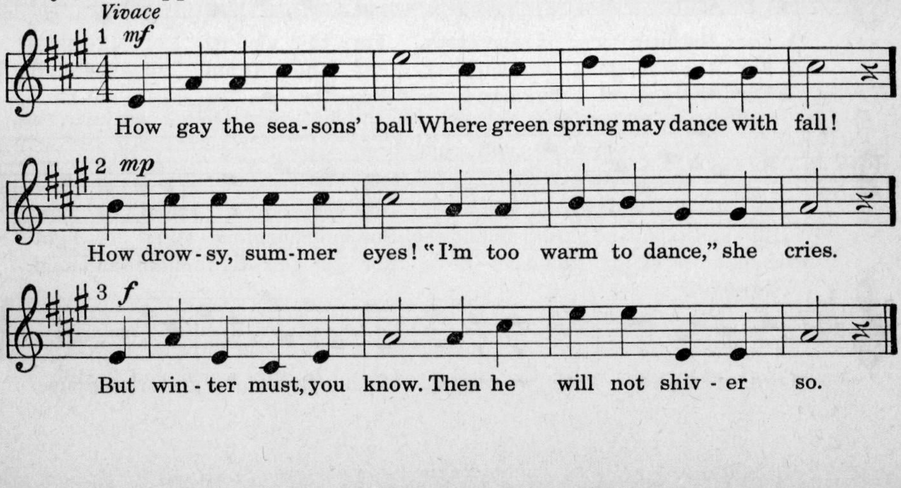
Vivace
1 mf
How gay the sea - sons' ball Where green spring may dance with fall!
2 mp
How drow - sy, sum - mer eyes! "I'm too warm to dance," she cries.
3 f
But win - ter must, you know. Then he will not shiv - er so.

Hymn of Praise

Caroline Atherton Mason — Herbert S. Irons

1. O God, I thank Thee for each sight Of beau - ty that Thy hand doth give, For sun - ny skies and air and light. O God, I thank Thee that I live.
2. That life I con - se - crate to Thee, And ev - er, as the day is born, On wings of joy my soul would flee, And thank Thee for an - oth - er morn;
3. An - oth - er day in which to cast Some si - lent deed of love a - broad, That, great'ning as it jour - neys past, May do some earn - est work for God.

Round: The Hillside

Marjorie Knapp — French-Canadian Folk Tune

Allegretto
1 f
Come, let us all go trip - ping Down the path be - side the hill.
2 mp
O - ver moss - y stones the brook is slip - ping, While we hear the mer - ry rob - ins trill.
3 mf
Flow'rs are bloom - ing, lambs are skip - ping In the sun - ny fields ly - ing warm and still.

Acknowledgments

THE EDITORS ARE UNDER DEEP OBLIGATION TO MR. E. W. NEWTON
FOR HIS VALUABLE SERVICE, WISE COUNSEL, AND ABLE LEADERSHIP

Acknowledgment is due also to Mr. Ennis D. Davis for assistance in establishing contacts with folk-song collectors in Europe and America; to Schroeder and Gunther, Inc. for permission to use the song "Summertime" by Victor Young; for the poem "The Little Turtle," from Vachel Lindsay's *Collected Poems*, by permission of The Macmillan Company, publishers; for the poem "Freckles," printed with permission from *Taxis and Toadstools* by Rachel Field, copyright 1926 by Doubleday, Doran and Company, Inc.; for the poem "The Scissors-Grinder," from *The Pointed People* by Rachel Field, copyrighted in 1930, used by permission of The Macmillan Company; to Theodosia Garrison for permission to use her poem "April"; to Frederick Warne and Company, Ltd. for permission to use the poem "The Broom and the Shovel," from Edward Lear's *Nonsense Book*; and for the Polish tune on page 149 and the Wendish tune on page 104, from *Das Lied der Völker*, Volume III, used by permission of B. Schott's Söhne, Mainz, Germany. The original illustrations are by Maud and Miska Petersham.

The editors appreciate the services of Louise Krueger and Harold Rugg in arranging the integration of these songs with the other curriculum subjects.

Alphabetical Index

PRINTED IN THE UNITED STATES OF AMERICA